INDIANS

POCAHONTAS, *Seymour*
PONTIAC, *Peckham*
SACAGAWEA, *Seymour*
SEQUOYAH, *Snow*
SITTING BULL, *Stevenson*
SQUANTO, *Stevenson*
TECUMSEH, *Stevenson*

NAVAL HEROES

DAVID FARRAGUT, *Long*
GEORGE DEWEY, *Long*
JOHN PAUL JONES, *Snow*
MATTHEW CALBRAITH PERRY, *Scharbach*
OLIVER HAZARD PERRY, *Long*
RAPHAEL SEMMES, *Snow*
STEPHEN DECATUR, *Smith*

NOTED WIVES and MOTHERS

ABIGAIL ADAMS, *Wagoner*
DOLLY MADISON, *Monsell*
JESSIE FREMONT, *Wagoner*
MARTHA WASHINGTON, *Wagoner*
MARY TODD LINCOLN, *Wilkie*
NANCY HANKS, *Stevenson*
RACHEL JACKSON, *Covan*

SCIENTISTS and INVENTORS

ALBERT EINSTEIN, *Hammontree*
ALECK BELL, *Widdemer*
CYRUS MCCORMICK, *Dobler*
ELI WHITNEY, *Snow*
ELIAS HOWE, *Corcoran*
ELIZABETH BLACKWELL, *Henry*
GAIL BORDEN, *Paradis*
GEORGE CARVER, *Stevenson*
GEORGE EASTMAN, *Henry*
GEORGE PULLMAN, *Myers*
GEORGE WESTINGHOUSE, *Dunham*
HENRY FORD, *Aird and Ruddiman*
JOHN AUDUBON, *Mason*
JOHN BURROUGHS, *Frisbee*
JOHN DEERE, *Bare*
LUTHER BURBANK, *Burt*
MARIA MITCHELL, *Melin*
ROBERT FULTON, *Henry*
SAMUEL MORSE, *Snow*
TOM EDISON, *Guthridge*
WALTER REED, *Higgins*

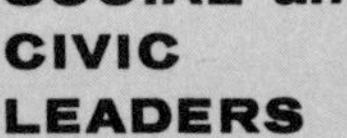

SOCIAL and CIVIC LEADERS

BETSY ROSS, *Weil*
BOOKER T. WASHINGTON, *Stevenson*
CLARA BARTON, *Stevenson*
DAN BEARD, *Mason*
DOROTHEA DIX, *Melin*
FRANCES WILLARD, *Mason*
J. STERLING MORTON, *Moore*
JANE ADDAMS, *Wagoner*
JULIA WARD HOWE, *Wagoner*
JULIETTE LOW, *Higgins*
LILIUOKALANI, *Newman*
LUCRETIA MOTT, *Burnett*
MOLLY PITCHER, *Stevenson*
OLIVER WENDELL HOLMES, JR., *Dunham*
SUSAN ANTHONY, *Monsell*

SOLDIERS

ANTHONY WAYNE, *Stevenson*
BEDFORD FORREST, *Parks*
DAN MORGAN, *Bryant*
ETHAN ALLEN, *Winders*
FRANCIS MARION, *Steele*
GEORGE CUSTER, *Stevenson*
ISRAEL PUTNAM, *Stevenson*
JEB STUART, *Winders*
NATHANAEL GREENE, *Peckham*
ROBERT E. LEE, *Monsell*
SAM HOUSTON, *Stevenson*
TOM JACKSON, *Monsell*
U. S. GRANT, *Stevenson*
WILLIAM HENRY HARRISON, *Peckham*
ZACK TAYLOR, *Wilkie*

STATESMEN

ABE LINCOLN, *Stevenson*
ANDY JACKSON, *Stevenson*
DAN WEBSTER, *Smith*
FRANKLIN ROOSEVELT, *Weil*
HENRY CLAY, *Monsell*
JAMES MONROE, *Widdemer*
JEFF DAVIS, *de Grummond and Delaune*
JOHN F. KENNEDY, *Frisbee*
JOHN MARSHALL, *Monsell*
TEDDY ROOSEVELT, *Parks*
WOODROW WILSON, *Monsell*

George Gershwin

Young Composer

Illustrated by Nathan Goldstein

George Gershwin

Young Composer

By Bernice Bryant

THE BOBBS-MERRILL COMPANY, INC.
A SUBSIDIARY OF HOWARD W. SAMS & CO., INC.
Publishers • INDIANAPOLIS • NEW YORK

LIBRARY OF CONGRESS CATALOG CARD NUMBER: 65-23666

PRINTED IN THE UNITED STATES OF AMERICA

Especially for
Ellis Bryant Zuckerman

Illustrations

Full pages

Contents

Books by Bernice Bryant

DAN MORGAN: WILDERNESS BOY

★ ★

George Gershwin

Young Composer

Street Music

It was a hot Thursday afternoon in the fall of 1904. George Gershwin sat at his desk in the first-grade room of Public School No. 20, on the East Side of New York City. It was a busy and crowded part of the big city.

The song of a rag man came through the windows:

"Any rags, any papers, any iron today,
A big fat man coming down your way."

George held his pencil loosely as he made big round O's on a sheet of ruled paper. Miss Abby, the teacher, walked slowly up and down to watch the first-graders practice their writing lesson. When she came to George, she said, "Good. You are doing much better with your writing today."

"That's because I'm writing my lessons to the music," said George.

"What music?" asked Miss Abby.

"The rag man's music," answered George.

Al, the biggest boy in the room, laughed. "Hank doesn't make music. He makes noise."

All the boys and girls giggled except Mike. Mike was George's best friend. George held his head high. He wasn't going to let anyone see that he minded Al making fun of him.

"Sh! Sh!" said Miss Abby.

Just then the school bell clanged the closing hour. The first-graders made ready to leave. As George rose, Miss Abby asked him to stay a minute. Then she followed the others from the room and left him waiting.

George waited and waited. "Why is she

making me stay after school?" he wondered. It was important that he and Mike have time to go to the new store building being built on Grand Street. Last evening they had seen two strong-looking sticks on the trash heap there. The sticks were just the right size and shape for playing hockey. The watchman said the boys would have to ask the foreman for them.

By now the sticks might be gone, George thought. If not, Al might see them and get them on his way home.

At last Miss Abby returned.

Clop, clop. Neigh, neigh. George listened to the fruit man's horse as it ambled by on the street outside. "Nice ripe bananas," drawled the fruit man.

"Is that music, too?" asked Miss Abby. "Or do you call that noise?"

George looked up. Was Miss Abby trying to catch him in some way?

"Maybe it's noise, but I like the noises of the streets," he answered. "They sound like music to me."

Miss Abby smiled. "I do, too. They are like new music—new music of a new world." She looked out the window as if she were listening to something. Then she said, "I must tell your mother about this. You may go now."

"Hmmm," George wondered as he rushed out of the room. "What will Mama say to that?"

At the school's entrance, Ira, George's big brother, was waiting.

"Did you see Mike?" asked George.

"He went on," said Ira.

"Then he will get the sticks," George thought hopefully.

"Why did you have to stay in?" asked Ira. He was a serious boy.

George turned his face to hide a smile. He would fool Ira. "Teacher made me," he said.

"What did you do?"

George chuckled. He followed Ira to the front of the big red building that faced Rivington Avenue. Al and a group of boys were playing hockey on the street.

"Did you hear more music?" Al called.

George didn't pay any attention to him, but turned down Forsyth Street.

Ira walked fast. "Let's get away from that trouble-maker."

"I'm not afraid of him," George said. "He has been mad ever since I won that race during recess last week. He thought he was the best runner in the room."

Al came after them. He whacked his hockey stick on the sidewalk and shouted, "Someday I'll beat you in a race."

George didn't even look back. He was in a hurry now. Maybe Mike was waiting for him on Grand Street by the new store.

The two boys walked along for several blocks. When they came to the new store building, George rushed back to the trash heap. It had been cleared away. The sticks were gone.

Disappointed, George trudged after Ira to their home. As they went through the cool area-way between the apartment buildings to the back yard, Ira said kindly, "I won't tell Mama you had to stay after school."

George's disappointment gave way to amusement. "Miss Abby is going to talk to Mama."

"Mama won't like that," said Ira.

At the top of the stairs, Gertie, the Gershwins' maid, was waiting for them.

"Did Mike call for me?" asked George.

"No." Gertie was nervous. "You boys take Art to the restaurant. I must hurry to be with my mother. She is ill again."

"Let me go with you," George offered.

"No, no," Gertie said. She opened the screen

door. "Run along now and change your clothes," she added.

George almost tore the stiff, hot school clothes from his body. He stepped into a pair of old overalls. Gertie awakened four-year-old Art from his nap and dressed him. "Come, Ira," she called. "We're all ready."

Ira came from the boys' room with a copy of *Do Or Dare* under his arm.

At the corner, Gertie continued north, but the boys crossed the street and walked on toward Broadway. Broadway was a noisy street crowded with shops, theaters, Penny Arcades, dance halls, and public baths. The Gershwin restaurant was on one corner. It belonged to Mama and Papa and Uncle Harry Wolpin.

As the boys approached the restaurant Mama came out on the sidewalk. "I saw you coming. Such a busy——"

Mama's mouth closed and her black eyes

grew large. Suddenly the air was filled with shouts of laughter and screams.

Al and his gang zoomed from an alley. A group of bigger boys followed them. Tins cans flew every which way. Hockey sticks crashed as the boys wrestled. The big boys laughed and shouted as they teased the smaller boys.

Little Art clapped his hands and ran into the street. He ran right into the midst of the big boys. Al yelled at him, shoved him aside, and knocked him down. Mama was watching. Her frightened scream rose above all the shouts and laughs.

George pushed through the mob of yelling boys, yanked Art away, and ran with him to the sidewalk. Al picked up a tin can and threw it at George. It landed on the curb.

Just then Mike came running up. "I got them!" He held the sticks high.

George grinned and grabbed one of them. It

felt good in his strong hands. He looked down at the tin can at his feet. He aimed and struck the can with all his strength. The can went hurtling to the end of the block.

"Hey, did you see that?" called the biggest boy, who was the leader of the group. Another battered can slithered to the curb, and again George took aim.

"Hold it! Hold it!" The big boy's voice was like a fog horn from the river. The other boys heeded him and became quiet. "Watch that kid," ordered the leader.

All eyes were on George as he took aim. He swung at the can and it, too, hurtled to the end of the block.

"That skinny little kid is good," said the leader. "Hey, what's your name?"

George didn't answer. He saw Al running down the street and laughed. "I knew he was afraid of me," he said. "I'll scare him some more." He took off after Al.

Al was far ahead and running hard. He looked back once, then disappeared behind a scraggly tree at the end of the block. When

George came to the tree, he suddenly stopped. Strains of low, thumping music were coming from a Penny Arcade near by.

George listened. He had heard that music before—last summer when Mama had taken him shopping on 125th Street. He sat down on the curb to listen. He didn't care where Al went now.

Over and over, the piano thumped out the music. It was strange music, but it made George feel glad and sad at the same time. He listened until the sun was going down behind the tall buildings. The scraggly tree began to look blue. Everything looked blue and beautiful, like the music, he thought.

At last he got up and ran back to the restaurant. "Where's Mike?" he asked.

"Mike had to go home," said Mama. "Go wash your hands. Our supper is waiting."

"Mike always has to go home," he thought.

The Gershwin family sat at a long table in the rear of the restaurant.

"Why did you stay down at that Penny Arcade so long?" asked Mama.

"I listened to blue music," said George.

"Blue music?" said Papa. "Whoever heard of blue music?"

"That reminds me," Mama said. "Miss Abby came into the restaurant while you were down the street, George."

Ira's big brown eyes stared. George's shoulders shook with giggles. He had fooled Ira.

Mama smiled. "Miss Abby said she thought you should be a musician."

"A musician in our family?" Papa laughed softly. "That's almost a joke."

Mike stepped into the restaurant. Mama invited him to have apple pie.

Mike was a quiet, mannerly boy. He answered Mama with "Yes, Ma'am" and "No,

Ma'am," and said no more. After supper he took George off to one side. "Stay away from Al," he whispered. "He said he was going to get the big boys to beat you up. He means it, too."

The threat didn't bother George. He wasn't afraid of Al. However, if Al knew what Miss Abby had said, he would tease George about it, and George didn't want that. He didn't want Al or anybody to tease him about music.

Birthday Surprise

ONE SATURDAY evening, George and Mike were in the alley behind George's home. They were practicing driving tin cans with their sticks.

Al came from a neighbor's back yard. "Hey, George, I can beat you in a race down to Broadway," he said.

"I don't want to race," George said. "I want to practice hockey. The big kids might let me play with them."

"Phooey! They wouldn't bother with you," Al said. "I dare you to race."

"You know George can beat you," said Mike. "He's the fastest runner in our class."

The boys had been promoted at the end of the school year. Next week when school started, they would be in the second grade.

"I double dare you," Al went on. "Or maybe you'd rather wait for the rag man's music."

At that George threw his stick in his back yard. "All right," he said. "We'll start from the end of the block." He ran toward the starting point.

"Just a minute," said Al as he ducked out of sight behind a shed.

At that moment Mike's mother called him to come home. His face puckered with a frown, but he said nothing and ran.

Several minutes passed before Al reappeared. Then he came skimming along the alley on a brand-new pair of roller skates. He stopped in front of George and cried,

> "One for the money, two for the show,
> Three to make ready, and four to go."

At the word "Go," Al spurted ahead.

For a second George was dumfounded. Then he called, "That's not fair. You're not running."

"I said I could beat you," Al called back. "I didn't say how."

George walked on. He was disgusted to think that Al had made a fool of him. He was lonely, too. "Why does Mike's mother always call him home?" he wondered.

Before long he came to the scraggly tree and turned in at the Penny Arcade. The automatic piano was quiet. It stood near the sidewalk in the open-front building. On the piano was pasted a chart listing the numbers and the names of selections of music. Beside the chart was a column of push buttons. Below the buttons was a slot for pennies.

George tried to read the names of the selections of music. The words were too hard. He pressed a button, but nothing happened.

He wished he had a penny. Papa had warned the boys against carrying money. "You might lose it," he had said. "Or big bullies might take it away from you."

Big bullies! George wasn't afraid. Next month he would be seven years old. Maybe he would get skates for his birthday and go skimming along the sidewalk. Then a better idea popped into his head. He turned and ran back home. He couldn't wait to tell his idea.

"I want roller skates for my birthday," he announced as he pushed open the kitchen door. "And a big party."

"Roller skates, yes," Mama said. "Party, no."

"Another year, son," said Papa. "We're too busy now, opening a second restaurant."

"A party would mean extra house cleaning and extra shopping. We haven't the time," explained Mama.

"Not for a family party," said Ira.

Mama was rocking Art. She leaned back and said softly, "It would be nice to have a big family party. We could have everyone there, including my parents, but Papa knows best."

Mama looked so tired, George thought. He wished they could have a party, not for him but for her, so that she could have a good time. Then he thought, "Why not surprise her? Why not give her a surprise party?"

He stepped to the calendar on the wall. It had a winter picture of a cabin in a forest. The snow in the picture felt sugary. At the bottom of the picture was the name, BRUSKIN FURRIER. George could read that name. Bruskin was Grandpa, Mama's Papa.

George lifted the August page of the calendar and looked for his birthday in September. It was the 26th, and it came on Tuesday. He would give the surprise party for Mama on the Saturday evening before his birthday.

George went to his room and counted the money he had in his matchbox bank. He had been saving for a paint set he had seen in a toy shop. Instead, he would spend his money for ice cream the night of the party. Tomorrow he would invite the relatives, he decided. They all lived in the neighborhood.

Mama had other plans for the next day, however. She took George and Ira shopping for new school clothes. Papa had plans for the day after that. He asked the boys to help the workers clean the old building in which the new restaurant would be located.

The rest of the week there was a steady rain, which kept the children off the street. Then school opened. Miss Carrie was George's teacher this year.

"Miss Carrie is nice, but funny-acting sometimes," Ira told George. "She has a wild temper and gives lots of homework."

George was so busy with homework that he didn't have a chance to invite the relatives until the morning of the Saturday on which he had planned the party. In his hurry he forgot to tell anyone that it was a surprise party for Mama.

Grandma Bruskin said, "Grandpa and I will be glad to come."

Uncle Harry thanked George for the invitation.

Young Aunt Kate said, "Good. I'll wear my new cheviot dress with the big puffed sleeves."

George was fidgety all the rest of the day. He counted his money at least six times.

Mama and Papa were late getting home from work and they felt very fidgety. Tomorrow was the grand opening of their new restaurant.

"We must all get to bed early tonight," Mama said when everyone had finished supper. "Ira and George, we'll need both of you to work at the grand opening tomorrow."

Just then there was a knock on the door. Ira answered it. Grandma and Grandpa Bruskin stepped into the kitchen, loaded with bundles.

"Rose, my child," Grandma said to Mama. "You are a wizard. Giving a party at such a busy time for you."

"Party?" Mama's black eyes opened wide. "Who is giving a party?"

Aunt Kate looked like a young lady in her new blue cheviot dress. Uncle Harry was behind her. He called, "Let's play Spin the Platter."

Papa's eyes were big, too. Ira gaped.

George bent over with giggles. He could hardly speak. "Surprise, Mama, surprise!" He threw his arms around her slim waist. "You said a family party would be nice."

Papa pulled out a chair from the table and Mama sank onto it. "George?"

"Surprise?" said Grandma. "George didn't say anything about a surprise."

"Really, Aunt Rose, didn't you know about the party?" asked her nephew, Henry Botkin.

Mama raised her hands. "And no refreshments in the house!"

George kneeled before her. "I thought of that, too," he said. "I have money for ice cream. Twenty-five cents."

Mama stroked his hair. "I shall always remember this nice surprise," she said chokily. She stood up. "Come, let's go into the parlor, or shall we play pinochle here in the kitchen?"

"We brought George some birthday presents," said Grandma. "My, he is getting to be a tall boy—almost as tall as Isidore. And he looks just like you, Rose, with his black eyes and jet black hair."

Papa laughed. "The surprise is on George."

George set about unwrapping the biggest package. He drew out an enormous Teddy Bear. At once the relatives began talking about

President Theodore Roosevelt, for whom this new toy had been named shortly before.

"He's the best President we ever had," said Uncle Harry.

"He's saving our forest land," said Grandpa. "That is good."

"He hunts bears," said George. He removed the paper from another package. "A paint set, just like the one in the window!" Next he unwrapped a Parcheesi game, and then he found his roller skates. He put them on immediately.

"Don't skate in the house," said Mama.

"I'll help George skate outside," said Papa.

Grandpa shuffled the cards. "Morris," he said, "you should learn to play pinochle." Morris was Papa's first name.

"No, thank you," said Papa. "Rose is the card player in our family."

George needed no help from Papa, but it was nice to have him sit on the front steps. He watched as George skated up and down and played a whiny tune on a fine-toothed comb wrapped in tissue paper. They stayed outdoors until Gertie came after them.

The pinochle game was over, and Grandpa was passing his hat around to the company. "For refreshments," he explained.

"Wait till I get my money," said George.

"I will pay for all," Papa offered.

"No," said Grandma. "We should get together like this often. By all sharing, no one takes the brunt of the cost of refreshments."

At the delicatessen Grandpa and George and Ira selected pickled herring and black bread and potato salad and hot blintzes. George especially liked the blintzes, crispy brown and covered with cottage cheese.

They had forty-two cents left over. "For you boys," Grandpa said as he divided the money evenly between them.

It had been a wonderful surprise party.

"I'm going to buy a new Horatio Alger book with some of my money," Ira said as they were getting ready for bed. "What are you going to do with yours?"

George shrugged his shoulders. He knew what he was going to do, but he didn't want to tell. Ira might think he was silly.

A Blue Picture

George felt in his shirt pocket. The money was still there. During lunch he had tied ten pennies in the corner of his handkerchief and had tucked the handkerchief into his pocket.

He smiled as he thought of his plan. As soon as school was out he was going to the Penny Arcade. With ten pennies he could play the song he had liked so much last summer on the mechanical piano. Just thinking about the song made his toes begin to wiggle.

Suddenly the voice of Miss Carrie, his teacher, interrupted his thoughts. "You are to draw a fall picture and color it," she said. "When the pictures are finished, we shall hang them in the school exhibit."

George straightened to attention. Miss Carrie passed out large sheets of white drawing paper. "Draw anything you wish," she suggested. "Trees or fall flowers or fruit, or perhaps a Thanksgiving scene."

"I'll draw the street," George decided.

He left the top half of the sheet of paper blank for the sky. In the lower half he drew apartment buildings and a scraggly tree. Then he drew a horse and wagon and some boys playing hockey.

He colored the sky blue. He colored the buildings blue and purple, the tree black, and its leaves blue. He colored the horse and wagon brown, shaded with blue. Then he held the picture up and studied it. He liked it.

When the pictures were finished, the children placed them on the blackboard rail at the front of the room. Mike put up a picture of a smiling clown. Soon there were pictures of purple grapes, red maple leaves, a witch, a Pilgrim, and a bright orange pumpkin. Finally George put his picture on the rail.

Al laughed at George's drawing. "It's just a jumble of blue and black marks," he said.

Miss Carrie looked at George's drawing and wondered, too. "What are those strange marks supposed to be?" she asked.

"A busy street," George explained. "The colors are the same as the colors of the music I hear in the streets." The more he tried to explain, the more the boys and girls laughed.

Miss Carrie took the drawing down from the rail and put it aside. "This drawing is too poor and unrealistic to include in the exhibit," she said coldly.

Al snickered and George closed his eyes tightly to keep from crying.

When the bell rang for recess, George lowered his head and filed out amid the giggling second-graders. In the main hall he dropped out of line and went to get his skates. Then he hurried out of the building to the far corner of the playground, crossed to the other side of the street, and walked on.

A block away he heard the bell ring and started to turn back. Then he stopped. No, he wasn't going back to school. He wasn't going to draw and color any more pictures. He wasn't going to let the children laugh at him. Still, if he went home Gertie would demand to know what had happened. What could he do?

Then he knew—the Penny Arcade! He would go there. He hurried toward Broadway, thinking happily about the song that he liked.

As he turned the corner on Broadway, near the Arcade, he almost bumped into a man. He looked up. The man was Uncle Harry Wolpin.

"Where are you going, George?" Uncle Harry asked. "Why aren't you in school?"

George's face turned red and he stood for a moment without answering. He didn't know what to say to his uncle.

"What's the matter?" Uncle Harry went on. "Don't you feel well?"

"Well, I—I—yes, I feel all right," George stammered.

Uncle Harry laughed. "Did the teacher send you home again?"

"N-no—well, not exactly."

"What do you mean, not exactly?" asked Uncle Harry suspiciously.

"Well, I—I just left. I got mad because the teacher wouldn't accept my drawing."

Uncle Harry frowned. "That wasn't the right thing to do," he said. "Don't you think you'd better go back?"

George shook his head emphatically. "I can't,

Uncle Harry," he said. "Not now. I just can't go back today."

"What are you going to do? Your mother ought to know about this."

"No, please, Uncle Harry," George said pleadingly. "I'll tell her later."

"Well, what are you going to do? You can't wander about the streets all afternoon." Uncle Harry thought for a moment. "I know. I'm going up to 125th Street to visit a friend and I'll take you along."

George was delighted. He had lived on 129th Street once, when his father and Uncle Harry had a restaurant a short distance away. He knew the neighborhood well. "I won't be any bother," he said. "I promise."

"Come on, then. Here comes a streetcar," Uncle Harry said.

They rushed into the street to board the car and soon were clattering along Broadway.

George looked with interest at the crowded street. It was filled with carriages and push-carts, and people jostled one another on the sidewalks. Broadway was a busy street, lined with theaters and Penny Arcades, restaurants and stores, hotels and apartment buildings.

At last Uncle Harry said, "Here we are!"

George followed him out of the car. Then he looked around. Once, he remembered, he had heard the song he liked somewhere near by. Where? It had come from a building with an open front, but that was all he could remember. He started across the street.

"Where are you going?" asked Uncle Harry.

"I'll just walk around here while you're visiting," said George.

"Don't be long."

George nodded and started westward. He had gone only a short distance when the high wail of a saxophone brought him to a stop. It

BARON WILKINS CLUB
Jim EUROPE'S BAND

was coming from an open doorway and was followed by the rat-tat-tat of a drum and the low thumping notes of a piano.

George went to the door and peeked in. Several musicians were seated in a circle, playing. George backed away from the door and sat on the curb to listen.

The music seemed to flow through his veins and all through his body. He wished he could make music like that.

Presently the music stopped. The musicians came out through the door and entered a nearby restaurant. George looked up at the building. A large sign beside the door said:

BARON WILKINS CLUB
JIM EUROPE'S BAND

George spelled out the words slowly. He did not know what they meant. He waited a while to see whether the musicians would return.

Then he went slowly back toward Broadway. The sounds of the music kept running through his head. He had never heard anything like it before and he wished it could go on forever. He felt as if he were moving in a dream.

Uncle Harry was waiting for him. George had little to say on the way home. He stared out the window of the streetcar and listened in memory to the sound of Jim Europe's band. It was better than the mechanical piano.

When they got off the streetcar at Grand Street, George started home without saying a word. "George," Uncle Harry called after him. "Where are you going?"

"Home."

"Don't forget to tell your mother."

George nodded without speaking and went on. When he reached the apartment building and started up the back steps, Ira called from the alley, "Where have you been?"

"What is a club?" George asked.

"It's something like a bat," Ira said. "You hit people with it."

"Not that kind," said George, suddenly feeling weak. He sank down on the bottom step.

Ira sat beside him. "Miss Carrie sent for me after recess," he said. "I've been looking for you ever since. She's mad because you left. She says Mama must come to talk with her."

"About what?" asked Mama as she and Papa appeared in the areaway.

George tried to explain about his picture.

"You say you colored a brown horse blue?" asked Mama. "Why?"

"Maybe George is color blind," Papa said. "What color is my tie, George?"

"Dark red," mumbled George.

"What color is——"

Mama broke in. "He's not color blind." She felt George's forehead for a fever.

"I'm all right," George said. "I just——"

"Did you ever see a blue horse?" Mama asked cautiously.

"Sure," George said. "Horses look blue sometimes—at least they do to me."

Mama frowned. "Morris, this child is sick." She led the family upstairs to the kitchen. She opened the kitchen cupboard and took out a bottle of brown medicine.

"I'm not sick," said George.

"Yes, yes, George, I know," Mama said. "Open your mouth."

"That's for babies. It says so." George pointed to the label on the bottle, which read, "Babies cry for it."

"Open your mouth," Mama ordered.

George gulped down the dose Mama held before him and went to his room. He crumpled on his bed, completely worn out, and closed his eyes. From far away, it seemed, he could hear

Papa's voice. "Don't worry, Mama. George is tired. Saturday was the party. Yesterday was the grand opening. We're all tired."

Mama was talking to Ira. "Miss Carrie didn't like his picture? She wouldn't show it?"

"How does she know?" asked Papa. "Maybe George will become a great artist and draw pictures nobody understands."

"Isidore, you go to Miss Carrie tomorrow and tell her George was sick," Mama said.

"But I'm not sick," George thought.

Even though he still felt weak the next morning, he was determined to go to school. He went early so that he could tell Miss Carrie he was sorry about leaving. Miss Carrie smiled as if nothing had happened.

"Did you say anything to her?" George asked Ira during recess.

"I did what Mama said, but I told you Miss Carrie acted funny sometimes," Ira said.

Al was the only person who said anything to George. When he wanted George and Mike to play hockey with him after school, George refused because he still felt wobbly.

"I guess you want to play hookey instead of hockey," jeered Al.

"Don't pay any attention to him," Mike whispered. All the while he sat beside George on a basement windowsill.

It was good to have a friend like Mike. He wasn't any good at skating or playing hockey, but he liked to listen to music and he knew what George meant when he talked about the peddlers' songs. He was a good friend who helped to make the days pass quickly.

The Ice Man and a Sissy

IT WAS the first day of vacation. Mike and George were sitting on the ground near the trash pile in George's back yard. It was a hot day—"hot enough to fry eggs on the sidewalk," Gertie had read in the morning paper.

The boys were waiting for Al. All three of them were to go wading in the playground pool.

"I have to play with him sometimes," Mike explained. "His mama and my mama are friends."

They heard the iceman's rickety wagon clattering over ruts and loose stones in the alley.

"Eye-eeze!" called the iceman.

"Eye-eeze!" mocked a shrill voice.

"That's Al," said George. He and Mike scrambled to their feet and ran to the alley.

The iceman "whoa-ed" his horse near George's back gate. Al jumped from the wagon. "The pool's closed this morning," he called.

The iceman lifted a thick, dirty white cover from the ice. The large glossy chunks of ice had frozen together. With a pick, the iceman loosened a large chunk from the mass. Chips of ice flew upward and down on the pavement, and the boys reached out to catch them.

Smack. Slurp. George could feel the cold ice sliding down his throat.

The iceman clutched a large chunk with tongs and carried it into the apartment building. Gertie would have the top of the icebox open, ready for the ice. Presently the iceman came out for another chunk, and then another. At last he was ready to go on. He tucked in the sides of the cover to keep out the heat.

The boys held to the back of the wagon and trotted after it. In the next alley the iceman stopped again to deliver orders. While he was in an apartment, Al hoisted himself up in the wagon. He crawled over the large mass of ice and scraped off jutting pieces.

Then he pounded and tugged and pushed with his feet until a large chunk split away. He shoved it from the wagon. It shattered into bits just as the iceman came back.

"Stealing!" shouted the iceman. "I let you boys hang onto the wagon. I give you chips of ice, and what do you do? Steal big pieces. How can I make money that way?"

"He did it," Al said, pointing to George.

"I didn't do it," said George. "You did."

Al's blue eyes were as innocent-looking as a kitten's. "There was no trouble until these two boys came. That one pushed a chunk from the wagon." Again he pointed at George.

The iceman clutched the back of George's overalls, almost lifting him from his feet. "You thief!" he scolded. "Where do you live? Your folks will have to pay for this."

"Let me go," George said. "I can prove I didn't steal the ice."

The iceman relaxed his hold a bit.

"Look at his ankle." George pointed to Al. "He scratched it against the ice. There's blood coming out of the scratch and there's blood up there on the ice where he scratched it. Isn't that true, Mike?"

Mike was too frightened to speak.

The iceman's eyes took in all that George had said. Al slipped around to the other side of the wagon. The iceman let go of George and turned to look at Al. He sprang after Al, shook him by the shoulder, and scolded.

"You lie, you steal. You grow up to no good. I'm going to take you home."

Mike and George stared as the iceman led Al, screaming, to his home.

"I'd better go home, too." Mike's face was white with fear.

"Mike is afraid of Al," thought George. "Why?" He himself was angry but not afraid. He trudged back down the alley to his home.

Gertie was in the kitchen kneading a big batch of yeast dough. She was making bread to take to her sick mother. Usually it was fun to watch her battle with the dough, but today somehow George wasn't interested.

"What's the matter with you?" Gertie asked.

"Oh, nothing," George said.

Presently Ira and Art came up the back steps together. They had come from a little book shop on Broome Street and had stopped at the playground along the way.

"I went wading," explained Art.

"Just for a little while," said Ira.

"Where?" asked George.

"At the playground," said Ira.

Then the playground wasn't closed! Al had lied about its being closed.

Ira took a book and went to the boys' room. George pushed open the screen door and sat on the back step. He felt lonely. Why did Mike have to go home anyway? Why was he afraid of that troublemaker Al?

Immediately after dinner, Ira went back to

his book. Gertie made ready to take Art out to get some new sandals.

"What are you going to do?" she asked. "Do you want to come with us?"

"No, I'll just skate around a bit," George said uncertainly.

After Gertie and Art had gone, George put on his skates and wandered around the neighborhood. Then, making a sudden decision, he headed toward Broadway. He would go to the Penny Arcade and listen to music.

When he reached the Arcade, the piano was playing the same song he had heard Jim Europe and his orchestra playing at the Baron Wilkins Club. George stood listening until the song was finished. Then he put a penny in the piano and played it again.

He had never forgotten that afternoon when he had sat in the doorway listening to Jim Europe's music. He could still see the drummer leaning over his drums, arms flying wildly, and he could still see the pianist's fingers dancing and marching over the keyboard. The power of the music had made the pianist seem like a giant of a man to George. Ever since then he had wished that he could play the piano himself.

When the song ended the second time, George put on his skates again and went home. All the way back to Forsyth Street he hummed the jerky tune. As he turned the last corner, he saw Al and a noisy group gathered in front of the apartment building.

"Sissy! You great big sissy!" Al sneered.

"Yes, sissy," called another boy.

Al minced about like a girl and cried in a mocking voice, "Go on home and practice your silly piano lesson."

Drawing closer, George saw that the boys were taunting Mike, who was following his sister. Was Mike taking piano lessons without letting him know about it? Well, why shouldn't he keep it a secret? Any boy who took piano lessons was a sissy. Or was he? Was the pianist at the Baron Wilkins Club a sissy?

"George, come over here," Al ordered. "You're on my side."

"I'm not on your side," George said firmly.

Al took his arm. "Oh, yes, you are." He pushed George forward.

George jerked his arm away and swung around. "Keep away from me! Can't you hear? I said I was not on your side."

Al stepped back quickly. His blue eyes actually looked scared.

"That's the way to handle a bully," George thought. Then he wondered whether Mike would let him play his piano. Of course if Al found out, he would tell the other boys and they would tease George, too. George wasn't sure whether he wanted that or not.

The Detective Steps In

EARLY THE next morning George called for Mike. Mike did not answer. George knocked on the door. No one answered, and George turned away, disappointed.

In the afternoon, he tried again to see Mike but got no answer. Every day that week he called for Mike.

One morning he told Ira, "I haven't seen Mike for a week."

Ira was lying on his bed, with an open book on the pillow. "Maybe he's away visiting someone," he said calmly.

George wished he could be like Ira. Ira never

got excited about anything. He could read for hours and be content and happy.

"You'd think Mike would have told me about leaving," George said. "He just disappeared."

At the word "disappeared" Ira sat up quickly. "Disappeared? Tell me the facts," he said in a business-like manner, closing his book and marking the place with a piece of yellow ribbon.

George glanced at the cover of the book. *A Study in Scarlet*, he read, by A. Conan Doyle. "Funny name for a book," he said.

"It's a detective story." Ira's voice was husky. "Sherlock Holmes solves the mystery of the murders."

"How do you know? You're only halfway through the book."

Ira's voice was natural now. "I've read this book two times already. It's the best book I've ever read in my life."

He got up, put on his cap with the bill

turned back, took a tablet of paper and a pencil from the table, and motioned for George to follow him. "Come, Watson," he said. "We'll solve the mystery of Mike's being gone."

"Why are you calling me Watson?" asked George.

For answer, Ira raised his eyebrows. Then he stalked out of the apartment, down the back steps and through the alley to Mike's apartment building. He tip-toed to the back door.

George followed him. "You sure are acting funny," he said.

"Sh-h." Instead of knocking on the door, Ira examined the door jamb.

"Look in the window," George suggested.

"My dear Watson, can't you see the shade on the window is drawn?"

George looked confused. "There's a little hole in the shade," he said, pointing upward. "It's too high for me to see through."

"Sh-h!" Ira made a tube of the tablet and held it to the window in front of the hole. "Aha! There's no furniture here," he said.

"No furniture! You mean Mike has moved?"

"Quiet." Ira examined the baseboard carefully. "There are marks here that show the furniture has been moved out."

"The furniture would have to be moved out if there's nothing in there," said George.

Ira ignored this explanation. "The mystery is solved. Mike is not here." He turned and headed home, his detective manner and voice gone. When he reached the alley he called, "The book is due today and there's another one there about Sherlock Holmes. I want to get it."

George laughed. "Some detective you are! Where's Mike? That's what I want to know." He knocked on the door of the next apartment.

An old woman opened the door a crack. When George asked about Mike, she told him that Mike's family had moved about a week before. "In the middle of the night," she said. "No one knows where." The door closed.

George was puzzled. Why would Mike's family move away in the middle of the night? The Gershwins had moved many times, too, because Papa liked to live near his business and he was always changing businesses. But they had never moved at night. George was glad Papa's two restaurants were near Forsyth Street. Maybe the family would never have to move again.

Mike's disappearance remained a mystery, but George came to know a great deal about the detective Sherlock Holmes and his assistant Watson. Before long the family was reading Ira's detective stories. At the Saturday night get-togethers everyone teased Ira, calling him Sherlock Holmes and George dear Watson, but the teasing was all in good fun.

One Saturday evening only Grandma and

Grandpa Bruskin came to visit. They sat in the kitchen talking with Papa and Mama. George was in the boys' room, but he could tell from their serious voices that they were worried.

"Morris, maybe you're biting off more than you can chew," said Grandpa.

"Maybe you're going in too deep," Grandma added. "You must be careful."

"Business is good," said Mama. "Morris and I have paid off almost all the debt on the first restaurant and some on the second. Now we are ready to go in debt on a third one. More people eat out every day. Profits are going up."

"But Rose, you must not work so hard."

"I love to work," said Mama. "We'll open the new restaurant this fall. Life is good to us, Mama. Soon we are going to move to a bigger apartment somewhere."

"Move!" blurted George. He rushed into the kitchen. "I don't want to move—not ever!"

"That is for Papa, to say, George," said Mama.

"Will we move in the middle of the night?"

"Gracious, no, child!" Grandma exclaimed. "Sometimes poor people who can't pay their rent sneak away in the night. Your parents would never do that, no matter how poor they were."

"Go back to your room, George," Mama said. "We are talking business."

Back in his room, George picked up his pocket knife and a piece of wood he had been whittling. Then he put them down again. He didn't feel like whittling any more.

He kept thinking of Mike. Were Mike's parents so poor they had to move in the middle of the night? Surely they weren't. They had a piano, and only rich people or almost-rich people had a piano. Still, Mike hadn't even said good-by to his friends. Hadn't Mike wanted to see his friends before he left? Would he ever come back again to see his friends?

The New Neighbors

THE DAY before school opened, the Gershwin family moved into a large apartment on Second Avenue. As soon as the furniture was in place, George put on his skates and went to explore the new neighborhood. He skated around the block, going faster and faster just to see how fast he could skate.

"What's your name?" called a short fat boy.

"Where do you live?" called a tall thin boy.

After supper George played with the boys. He made friend with them quickly. When he went to bed that night he told Ira, "I didn't think I would like living here, but I do."

The next morning Mama asked the boys whether they knew the name of their new school.

George answered for both boys. "It's Public School 25 and it's located at First Avenue and Second Street."

"Isidore, you must take Art," said Mama.

"I have to take some books back to Broome Street first," said Ira.

"I'll take Art," said George. "Ira took me when I was little and now I'll take Art."

George put on his skates and set off with Art. Sometimes he darted ahead of Art and sometimes behind him.

"Hi, George," called John and Oliver, and George smiled and waved in return. It made him feel good to know that he already had friends in the neighborhood.

When he reached the school, he took Art to the first-grade room and left him with the teacher. Then he went to the third-grade room.

Miss Josephine, the teacher, told the children where to sit in the room. Then she said, "Every morning we shall begin the day with singing." She waved a ruler to lead the children as they sang "Loch Lomond."

One voice in the group had a low, throaty sound that drew George's attention during the singing. He looked around to see whose voice it was and noticed a thin girl with silky blonde hair standing at the back of the room. She was smiling and holding her head high as she added extra, rippling notes to the melody.

When the chorus began, George's fingers thumped against his desk to her extra notes.

"You take the high-igh road,
And I'll take the low-ow road,
And I'll be in Scotland before you-oo."

George wondered how she jiggled the words in such a pleasing manner. When the song ended, he blurted, "Let's sing it again."

"We'll sing 'Loch Lomond' again tomorrow," said the teacher.

It was hard for George to think about arithmetic with the tricky sounds of the girl's voice thumping around in his head. By recess time he had forgotten about playing with his new friends and followed the girl from the building to a shady side of the playground.

He had already learned that her name was Mamie. Miss Josephine had called her Mamie when she asked her to read.

"Where did you learn to sing that way?" he asked Mamie on the playground.

"That's the way my Mama plays the piano," she said. She held her head high and began the chorus of "Loch Lomond."

"Hey, George! Come on and play," called John.

"We're ready to start," added Oliver.

"I'll be there in a minute," answered George.

Mamie laughed. Her laugh was rippling and low, like her singing.

When recess ended the boys and girls fell in line to return to the room. John snickered, "George likes the girls." The children giggled and George hung his head.

In the classroom George tried to study, but the rippling sounds of Mamie's voice stayed with him. At noon, he avoided the others and waited for Art. Again he skated around Art, going home, but this time the boys didn't talk to him. After school they didn't come near him, either. He and Art walked home alone.

Two blocks from home they met Mamie at a corner where two streets crossed. "Would your Mama play for me sometime?" he asked.

"Oh, yes. Come in now." Mamie skipped ahead, up a flight of stone steps.

Her mother had the same rippling laugh that Mamie had. "We'll have a concert," she said.

She invited George and Art into the parlor. "Just call me Mrs. Choo. Nobody can pronounce our long name."

She moved the piano bench away, then sat down, bowed to her small audience, and began to play. George couldn't sit still. He stepped up beside the piano and watched Mrs. Choo's fingers fly across the keys.

"Let me play, please?" he asked presently.

"Oh, do you play the piano?" said Mrs. Choo, pushing the bench closer to the piano.

"No, but I'd like to try," said George. He sat before the piano and rested his fingers on the keys. He struck one note, then another, and another. The tune of "Loch Lomond" was whirling inside him as Mamie had sung it. It seemed to push through his fingers as if they knew exactly where to go to make the lilting sounds come from the keys of the piano.

He played the piece again and again.

Mrs. Choo interrupted his playing. "You say you never played a piano?" she asked.

"No." George was shaking with joy. "Oh, I want to play."

"Come and play here any time you want to," said Mrs. Choo.

Any time he wanted to! He'd be back soon.

That evening at the supper table he said, "I wish we had a piano."

"Who would play it?" asked Papa.

"Some day soon I want Isidore to take music lessons," said Mama.

"Oh, Mama, I don't want to be a sissy!" Ira said disgustedly.

"Nobody would have to know if I took lessons," George thought to himself. "Maybe Mrs. Choo will teach me."

When George mentioned his idea of taking lessons to Mamie later, Mamie said, "Mama can't read music. She plays by ear."

Mrs. Choo was willing to teach George. "You have an ear for music," she said.

Evening after evening George and Art walked home with Mamie. Art enjoyed going because he could always have candy or peanuts at Mamie's house, but he didn't understand that George was taking music lessons.

The boys and girls in George's class snickered and made fun of him, but he hardly noticed them. He hardly noticed that the boys had stopped asking him to play games after school.

One October evening Oliver told him he was girl-crazy. "I'm not any such thing!" George flared in reply, hurrying along the walk to catch up with Mamie.

"I wouldn't be crazy about any silly old girl," he thought. "Maybe I'm crazy about music, but I'm not girl-crazy." Still, he couldn't help wondering what the boys would do if they found out he was taking music lessons.

When Mamie opened the door for George and Art that afternoon, the apartment was fairly dancing with Mrs. Choo's music. "Put your arms around me, honey," she sang.

George's fingers and toes twitched in time to the tricky beat. This was the new song he had heard at the Penny Arcade on Broadway.

"Let me try it," he said.

Mrs. Choo rose, stepped to the window, and raised it a bit.

The fingers of George's right hand groped for the proper keys.

"Now the left hand, George," said Mrs. Choo. "Beat, beat, beat——"

After several tries, George cried, "I got it!" He began to play with gusto, and the little group began to sing, "Put your arms around me, honey."

George's shoulders shook with amusement. Mama would be surprised to see him now!

At last Mrs. Choo said, "It's almost five o'clock, George, time for you to go home."

Mamie went to open the front door. As he stepped outside George was greeted by another song, sung in a familiar high voice.

> "George is a sissy, George is a Maggie,
> Put your arms around me honey,"

George looked down into the faces of Al and the boys from his new school. Al was dancing around in imitation of a girl.

> "Georgie, Porgie, puddin' and pie,
> Kissed the girls and made them cry."

George lunged from the top step and knocked Al to the sidewalk. "Be quiet, do you hear?" he shouted angrily. "Say you'll keep quiet!"

"I'll keep quiet," Al gasped.

George looked up. "You heard him, didn't you?"

The group held back with admiration. George

jumped up, gave Al a shove, reached for Art's hand, and walked away fast.

Oliver came running after him. "Let's play Cat, George."

"I'll play with you tomorrow," said George. He breathed deeply to keep from crying. He was angry with Al, with himself, and with the whole world. Why had he taken music lessons in the first place? He should have known he couldn't keep them a secret. Yet why couldn't a boy take music lessons without being made fun of? What kind of world was this?

Fighting George

THE NEXT evening George played hockey with the Seventh Street boys. He was determined to show them he wasn't a sissy. Within a week he had become the leader of the group. He was the best hockey player, the best skater, and the best fighter. He would never go to Mamie's house and never think of music again.

More than once in the weeks that followed he came in to supper with his overalls torn. "You're always fighting," Mama scolded.

"Son, can't you try to get along with the other boys?" Papa asked.

"I'm the leader and they have to get along

with me," George said. He sounded like a different boy from the boy who enjoyed music. He even neglected to take care of Art.

"What is troubling you?" asked Papa in a kindly voice one Saturday morning.

"Jimminy crickets, leave me alone," George answered gruffly. "Nothing's troubling me." He pushed his cap far back on his head and swaggered out of the apartment.

Outside, he huddled in a corner under the back stairs. He couldn't tell Mama and Papa what bothered him, because he wasn't sure himself. He just knew he wanted to make music. When he didn't make music or hear music he felt ugly, and he treated others in an ugly way.

He was rude to Gertie when she quit to live with her sick mother. He was rude to the new maid, Mabel. He grumbled about his new baby sister, Frances, whom everyone called Frankie.

"She's a crybaby," he said.

"All babies cry," said Mama. "Come rock her."

"Nah, I'm not a woman."

"That's no way to talk," said Papa sternly.

"George is always using slang," said Mama.

Papa's voice softened. "George, this evening you and I are going out."

"Where?" asked George.

"You'll see."

At seven o'clock Papa told George to put on his overcoat. They went over to Broadway and down Broadway until they came to a dark brick building. Many people were gathered at the entrance, waiting to go in.

"A concert!" George said in surprise. He looked around quickly, hoping none of the neighborhood boys would see him. They probably wouldn't, because most boys didn't attend concerts willingly. Inside, he slumped in his seat and held his head low to keep out of sight.

When the music began, it took away the anger

that had been with him so long. He wished the music would never end.

Going home he laughed and talked with Papa. "I'll rock Frankie," he offered when he stepped into the kitchen. He saw Mama smile at Papa and felt good.

From that time on George and Papa and sometimes Ira attended the concerts regularly. Listening to the music did not entirely satisfy George because he wanted to make music, too, but it helped.

All the while he stayed on as leader of the Seventh Street boys. They didn't find out that he was attending concerts.

In April all the pupils of Public School 25 were invited to attend the Spring Program. Maxie Rosenzweig, known as a child prodigy, was to play the violin.

"Listen, fellows, we're invited to hear that sissy," George explained the afternoon of the program, "but that doesn't mean we have to go." He and his friends were playing ball in a far corner of the school playground.

"Only sissies want to listen to that little sissy," said Oliver. "I remember when he went to school here."

"Sure," said George. He took hold of the bat, stepped to the plate, and swung as the pitcher threw the ball. *Crack!* The ball flew over the heads of the fielders and George's long legs scampered around the small diamond.

"Home run!" shouted George's team. "George did it again!"

George calmly walked over to the fence and sat down. He wanted his team to win.

By now dark clouds were gathering in the sky and it was threatening to rain. A flash of lightning and a roll of thunder brought down a smattering of big drops, but the boys went on playing. It was fun to play in the rain.

George was pitching at the time. He rubbed the ball between his hands. Suddenly he heard beautiful violin music drifting from an open window. He looked up and stared.

"Come on, throw the ball!" called Oliver.

The music swelled with power. George wished he had the courage to leave.

"Hey, George, play ball!" shouted John.

His voice made George edgy. "Be quiet," he ordered. Then as the music gave him courage, he threw the ball to the ground, turned, and walked toward the building.

"Where are you going? What are you doing?" the boys demanded, but George ignored them. He stood beneath the window like a statue, listening to the strains of the music.

When the concert ended, he hurried to the front of the building, hoping to meet Maxie. Parents and children in their best clothes crowded out the door. The rain was steady now.

George stood close to the door watching for a boy with a violin case. The crowd thinned. A few stragglers came from the building. The sky turned white with another flash of lightning. There was another roll of thunder, and the rain came down in torrents.

George tried the door. It was locked so that

people could get out but could not get in. He rattled the door. He pounded on the window sill. He had to see Maxie.

After a long time the janitor called from inside. "What do you want?" he asked.

"I want to see Maxie," George called.

"He went home," said the janitor.

"How? When?" asked George.

"About an hour ago. Some of the teachers took him. They went out the teacher's door."

"Oh." George's voice fell. Then he added, "Where does he live? I want to see him."

"Let me think. Uptown—what's that street? It's the building next to——" The janitor mumbled on. "Wait a minute. It's on the program."

The janitor started down the basement stairs. "Ah, here's one." He picked up a program that had fallen to the floor, opened the door, and handed it to George.

"Thanks." George crouched against the building to keep the program dry. On the back page was a story about Maxie, also his address. George smiled. He would go to see Maxie. Something seemed to drive him on.

He turned up his collar and trudged through the rain. He zigzagged over to Third Avenue, where the elevated railroad tracks overhead helped to protect him from the downpour.

Presently the rain slackened. The thunder sounded far away, but the clouds hung low and gray. Darkness came early.

At last George reached the building and found his way up to Maxie's apartment. A kind-looking woman opened the door.

"My, what's this?" she said. "A drowned rat?"

Water dripped from George's clothes and made a puddle in the hall. "I want to see Maxie," George said.

Mr. Rosenzweig came to stand behind his wife. "Are you a friend of Maxie?"

"No, but I surely want to be," said George. "I heard him play today."

"Maxie's not here," said Mrs. Rosenzweig.

"Oh." George was disappointed.

"Where do you live?" she asked.

George mumbled his address.

"So far?" the Rosenzweigs said together. "You must come in and have some milk before you start back home." Mrs. Rosenzweig led George through a richly carpeted hall to a bright kitchen. She sliced cake and poured milk into tumblers.

Between bites George told of his desire to play music.

"You must come when Maxie is home," said Mrs. Rosenzweig. "Can you come Sunday?"

"I surely can," said George.

It was still raining when George left Maxie's parents, but the whole world seemed sunny to him. Sunday afternoon he would spend with Maxie, the child prodigy.

Best Friend

SUNDAY AFTERNOON George dressed in his best clothes. "I'm going to Maxie Rosenzweig's house," he announced.

"Isn't that the boy who plays the violin?" Mama asked.

"He's a sissy," said Art. "Why do you want to be friends with him?"

George's cheeks grew warm. Art was saying what the boys at school would say. However, George wanted to play music and this time he wasn't going to care what anyone said. He picked up his skates and left.

Maxie was waiting for him in the soft carpeted hall. George could scarcely believe that this famous boy was so little.

"What was that piece you played at school?" George asked. "It was great!"

Maxie's brown eyes grew bright. He was not used to having boys enjoy his music. "I suppose you mean Dvorak's 'Humoresque,' " he said. "It is a simple melody that appeals to the popular ear." Big words slid from his tongue as easily as slang rolled from George's. "Anton Dvorak was a Bohemian composer."

George stared. He had never heard anyone talk this way before.

Maxie stepped to the piano and fingered the keys. The sweet melody filled the room.

"Hey, let me try to play it," George said.

"Are you a musician, too?" asked Maxie.

"I want to be," said George. He sat before the piano and felt for the right keys.

"Do you read music?" asked Maxie.

"No, I just feel it out," answered George. After several tries, he played a simple version of "Humoresque."

"This is strange," said Maxie. He lifted his violin from its case on the piano. With a sure touch he followed George's unsure playing. George had never been so happy.

"You seem to have a natural talent that should be developed," said Maxie.

George laughed. "I'll learn to play the piano real well and then we can go on concerts together," he said.

"Yes, let's do that."

"We'll go to schools and clubs, even play with the Philharmonic Orchestra." George could almost see himself seated on a big stage.

"We'll travel to all the music capitals—Dresden, Budapest, Milan——"

"Sure, sure, all those places," George had never heard of music capitals, but he was eager to go anywhere with Maxie. Their daydreams made the afternoon pass quickly.

After that all the days passed quickly for George. Maxie had opened a door and shown him a whole new world, a world of music, in which Maxie was a master.

"Beethoven was the composer of this piece," Maxie said one hot Sunday afternoon in July. The boys were in the Rosenzweigs' cool parlor, and Maxie was playing a section of "Minuet in G" on his violin. "When Beethoven grew old he became deaf," he explained to George, "but he continued to compose music."

Compose and composer—those were new words for George. "You mean that music came out of his head?" George asked.

"Out of his head and his heart," said Maxie.

"I'm going to be a composer," said George.

Maxie smiled. The lively strains of "Minuet" gave way to the stately strains of "Sarabande."

"Handel composed this," said Maxie. "He was born in Germany but later moved to England."

"Does he still live in England?"

"Handel died a long time ago."

Maxie began to play a low, thumping melody. George sat up straight. This was the music he had heard on 125th Street when he was a little boy. He had heard it on the automatic piano.

"Who composed that?" he asked.

"This is 'Melody in F' by Anton Rubenstein," said Maxie.

George sat quietly until Maxie finished. "I want to try to play that." He stepped to the piano. His fingers groped for the right keys.

"You have to learn to read music," said Maxie.

George tried again and again. The melody came to him. He thumped a steady beat with his left hand. It sounded good to him.

"George, people don't play Rubenstein that way," Maxie said. "That sounds too much like ragtime. You must play the music the way it was written. Play it like this."

George listened to Maxie's perfect playing. He would try to play it that way. He wanted to follow Maxie in every way possible. Maxie didn't like popular music, so George wouldn't like popular music. Maxie didn't play hockey, so George wouldn't play hockey. Maxie didn't use slang, so George wouldn't use slang.

George struggled through several bars of music according to Maxie's instructions. Then the clock on the mantel struck four. Maxie would have to get ready for a concert rehearsal that evening. George rose to leave.

"You're a smart boy," he said.

"I've studied music as long as I can remember," said Maxie. "You're smart in other ways—in playing hockey or baseball."

"But I want to play the piano," said George.

On his way home he met John and Oliver.

"You never play with us any more," said John.

"I think Al from your old neighborhood was right," added Oliver. "You're a sissy." He seemed to want to make George angry.

George tightened his fists but tried not to show his anger. "I've been busy," he said, as he skated on. It would be fun to play hockey again, he thought. He felt restless.

Maxie would be gone during the month of August. George wondered what he would do without him—and without a piano. Maybe Mama and Papa would get a piano now. He would ask them tonight.

As he went up the back stairs he could hear Frankie crying. Mama was walking back and forth through the long hall, holding Frankie over her shoulder to quiet her.

"Frankie's got the colic," said Art.

"Shall I go for the doctor?" asked George.

"Mabel went for medicine," said Mama.

"Let me rock her," said George.

Mama placed the baby in his arms. "I'll get some supper."

George carried the baby into Mama's darkened bedroom. He lay her across his lap and jiggled his knees to a melody that had come into his head. Presently she closed her eyes in sleep.

Papa and Ira came home. Several minutes later Mabel brought the medicine. The family sat down for dinner.

George told how he had quieted the baby. "I hummed to her and jiggled my knees. If we had a piano, I would play for her."

"Oh, phooey!" said Art. "Real boys don't play the piano. Everybody says you're a sissy, running around with that Maxie."

The anger George had held in so long now flared openly. "I don't care what anyone says!" he said, jumping up. As he backed away from the table, he knocked his chair over with a crash.

Frankie woke up and began to cry. Mama scolded, and George stomped off to his room and sat on his bed. Ira followed him.

"Why don't you calm yourself, George?"

By now George's sudden anger was gone and he felt ashamed. He wished he could be calm like Ira, who didn't worry about the boys. Ira just went about quietly, going to the library and reading books. He didn't like hockey.

George went back to the kitchen. "I'll play hockey with you right now," he told Art.

They played until dark. When they returned to the quiet apartment, Papa was at the table with papers and books before him. He looked up and motioned for George to come to him.

"Business is good, son," he said. He reached up and pulled George's head down. "I think this fall we can get a piano," he whispered.

"Papa! Oh, Papa!" was all George could say.

A High Hat

SINCE SIX o'clock this Labor Day morning, the Gershwins had been getting ready for a picnic at Coney Island.

"Put everything you're going to take in this corner," said Mama. She was in a dither.

One corner of the kitchen was already stacked high. Mabel was wrapping crisp brown pieces of fried chicken in wax paper and placing them in a shoe box. Mama was packing potato salad in a stone jar.

Honk, honk, honk.

"Uncle Harry's here!" George cried. He rushed to the parlor and looked through the stiffly starched lace curtains. A shiny black automobile stood in front of the apartment building with Uncle Harry at the wheel.

Uncle Harry looked like a moving picture hero with his dark goggles almost covering his face. He stepped down from the running board of the shiny automobile, and his long driving coat swished about his legs.

When George turned to go back to the kitchen he passed the parlor door and noticed that his mother had arranged an open place along a wall. A smile came to his face, because he knew why. Papa had said he could have a piano in the fall. The piano might come any day now.

"George, come help carry the bundles," Mama called from the kitchen.

"Give the bundles to me and I'll put them on the running board," said Uncle Harry.

"Let me blow the horn." George climbed to the front seat, stretched his arm to the side of the windshield and squeezed a rubber ball that made the horn honk.

Mama came from the areaway. She looked stylish in her silk riding coat. She had on goggles, too. So had Papa.

"I'll be lonely without the baby," Mama said a little sadly.

"The baby will be better off with Mabel at home," said Papa.

Uncle Harry turned the crank to start the automobile. The engine shivered. It sputtered. It started to run. Quickly Uncle Harry climbed into the automobile. He started it and steered it around wagons and pushcarts and people. He drove proudly across Brooklyn Bridge, south through the borough of Brooklyn, out onto the new shell road that led to Coney Island.

The wind whipped through the open car. Mama called, "Don't go so fast."

George leaned forward to look at the speed-

ometer. "Twenty-five miles an hour! Hoop-de-doodle, that's fast!"

"Stop speeding," called Mama.

Near the Boardwalk Uncle Harry stopped the automobile. The motor quieted and the sounds of the island swelled.

The sounds were like the music of a giant orchestra, George thought. There were the calliope of the merry-go-round, the rumble of the roller coaster, and the squeak-squeak of the Ferris wheel. There were the cries of the barkers and the vendors. There were shots from the shooting galleries and swishes of splashing waves on the beach.

George started to run across the sand toward the water, when somebody called to him. "George! Hey, George Gershwin!"

George turned to find Mike, who had moved in the middle of the night, sitting on the beach. The next minute the two boys were hugging each other like long-lost friends. They laughed and jumped up and down in the sand.

"Where did you go?" asked George. "Do you still play the piano? I'm going to take lessons."

"We live here on the island," said Mike. "My Pop is doing real well now, paid all his bills. He runs the Ferris wheel. He'll give us free rides. Yes, I play the piano." Mike wasn't a bit afraid to say he played the piano.

"George, don't get your shoes wet," called Mama from her blanket.

George and Mike ran back to where the blankets and bundles were spread out on the sand. "Mama, this is Mike. I found him here."

All the Gershwins remembered Mike. Once again he became a member of the family.

Swimming came first. "You can't go into the water for one hour after you eat," said Mama.

"No ocean for me," said Papa. "I want to try a Turkish Bath on the Boardwalk."

During the early afternoon Mike guided the Gershwin boys around the amusement park. "There's Pop," he said proudly as they neared the Ferris wheel.

"Well, well, the Gershwin boys," said Pop. "You must ride on the largest Ferris wheel in the country."

Four giggling ladies stepped from the car closest to the ground. Pop motioned for the boys to step into the empty car. He pulled a lever on a box at his side and the giant wheel turned. The car rocked. Squeals of excitement mingled with the squeak of the grinding wheel.

Art was afraid and clung to Ira. George sat stiffly, chiefly in wonderment. As the car went up, all the sounds of the island seemed to gather around him, yet each sound was clear and distinct. At the very top he heard a tinkling piano and a man singing. He wondered where the sounds came from and wanted to find out.

The car went down, down, down. The piano and singing became less distinct. Then the car went up again and once more they became clear and catchy.

At last the ride ended. "Come and ride again," Pop said as the boys left.

"I heard someone singing and playing a piano," George said.

"That's Dobey, the song plugger," said Mike. "I take piano lessons from him."

"Song plugger?"

"Dobey sings the new songs and people buy the sheet music," Mike explained. "That's the way new songs get to be popular."

"Let's ride the merry-go-round," said Art.

"I want to see Dobey," said George.

Mike led the boys through the crowd to a small open booth on the Boardwalk. Here they found a group of people listening to a singer who was wearing a straw hat.

"Anything you want to hear," the man was saying. "Just name it. I'll sing and play anything you mention."

" 'After the Ball Is Over,' " called a fat man.

Dobey lifted his hat, bowed, and sat at the piano. With a great flourish his fingers moved across the keys. When he had finished, he rose, bowed, and said, "There you are, and here's the sheet music. Fifteen cents, please." He offered the sheet music to the man who had asked to hear it sung.

"Anything you want to hear," Dobey said.

" 'Melody in F' by Rubenstein," called George.

"Ha, ha, ha," laughed Dobey. "We have a high hat in our midst. Sonny, there are no words to Rubenstein." He noticed that George was with Mike. "Mike, who's your high-hat friend?"

"This is George Gershwin," said Mike.

Dobey bowed very low. "For George Gershwin, I shall play 'Melody in F.' " Dobey looked at the audience and winked. He started to play the thumpy melody.

"He's playing it the way Maxie said I should play it," George thought.

Soon Dobey began to bounce up and down on his chair. He turned to the audience and winked again. The rhythm changed and his left hand beat out notes like a drum.

George's heart beat, too. "That's the way I wanted to play the piece," he thought.

"Come on, George, we want to do other things," said Ira.

"You take Art," said George. "I'm going to stay here a while." He and Mike sat on the floor at Dobey's feet and listened. He wondered who composed popular music and who wrote the words. He was enjoying himself so much that he did not notice the sky was growing dark.

Soon Ira came edging through the thinning audience. "Come on, George," he said, tapping

George on the shoulder. "Mama says we have to go. There's a storm coming up."

"I wish you didn't have to go," said Mike.

"I wish you didn't live so far away," said George. He and Ira hurried back to the family. Mama hustled the boys into the automobile. Papa and Uncle Harry fastened the black curtains to its sides. The tiny isinglass windows in the curtains gave little light.

"Just a minute," said Uncle Harry. "A person can't come to Rabbit Island without getting a hot dog." He headed toward the Boardwalk.

"Where's Rabbit Island?" asked Art.

"We're on Rabbit Island," said Papa. "A coney is a rabbit. Years ago this island was thick with rabbits."

Several minutes later Uncle Harry returned carrying a paper bag. "Hot dogs for all," he said, giving the bag to the others.

"These aren't dogs," Art said, disappointed.

Mama and Papa laughed.

"I heard that old Charles Feltman made a fortune selling these frankfurters and buns here," Papa said.

"Feltman was a smart man," said Uncle Harry. "Another five years and hot dogs will be popular all over the country."

He started the car and the family were soon on their way home. As the car bounced over Brooklyn Bridge in the rain, Mama and Papa and Uncle Harry began to sing a song.

"Come away with me, Lucile,
In my merry Oldsmobile——"

George's shoulders swayed. His fingers played on an imaginary keyboard. Soon he would be playing a real piano!

Six weeks later, however, Papa said sadly, "I'm sorry, George, but we can't get a piano this fall. Business has been bad."

Heartbreak and Hot Dogs

ONE COLD Saturday night, late in October, the Gershwin family sat around the kitchen table in the apartment with Grandpa and Grandma Bruskin. Papa's forehead was furrowed and Mama's eyes were dull from worry. "Times are hard, George," said Papa. "We can't get you a piano this fall." George's throat choked and he was speechless.

"Morris, what can we do?" asked Mama.

"We'll have to close the last restaurant we opened," Papa said.

"I don't understand all this," said Grandma. "Just a few months ago you were doing so well.

You opened a third restaurant and moved into this big apartment. Now—no money. How could things change so quickly?"

"The country is going through a business panic," Grandpa explained. "Some of the banks loaned too much money to big businesses. Now they don't have enough to give to other customers who come in to draw out money."

"Don't you have any money?" asked Grandma, turning to Papa.

"Not enough to pay the mortgage, and I can't get a loan," said Papa. "The panic is spreading throughout the country. People everywhere are taking their money out of the banks, and the banks are closing."

"Is your bank closed?" asked Grandma.

"No, but it can't loan me money," said Papa. I must close the third restaurant."

"I hope we can keep the other two restaurants," said Mama, "but the wages take so much."

"People don't have much money to eat in restaurants now, either," Papa added. "They think twenty-five cents is too much for a dinner, but we can't serve them for less."

"Morris and Rose, do not worry," said Grandpa. "President Roosevelt will help solve the bank problem. This panic won't last long. Our country is rich and strong, and everything will turn out all right. Maybe there will be better banking laws."

Mama had tears in her eyes. "We'll have to work harder, Morris."

George had backed out of the kitchen and into the parlor, a room that was rarely used. He sat on the sofa across from the space that had been cleared for the piano. He stared at the area of dark red flowered wall paper. His fingers drummed against the green velvet sofa.

The song the family had sung about the merry Oldsmobile came to him, along with other thoughts of that wonderful day at Coney Island. The sounds, the smells, the sights went through his head. He could even taste the hot dogs.

Hot dogs! An idea came to him. In a moment he jumped up and rushed to the kitchen. "Papa, if twenty-five cents is too much for a dinner, give the customers a five-cent dinner."

"And lose more money?" asked Mama.

"No, make money like that man did at Coney Island. Serve hot dogs."

"George, a hot dog sandwich is no lunch for a hungry man," said Mama.

Papa spoke up. "Rose, George has given me an idea. We could serve hot dogs and some-things else like——"

"Beans," Grandma broke in.

Papa thought out loud. "A special plate—fifteen cents. A hot dog sandwich, coffee——"

"And beans," put in Grandma again.

"Yes, beans," called Ira from the boys' room.

He and Art were playing checkers, but Ira's ears were tuned to the kitchen.

"Baked beans," called Art.

"That's it! We could do it and make money," said Papa.

Grandpa ruffled George's black hair. "This boy has a business head on his shoulders."

"Papa, I could work in the restaurants after school and on Saturday," said George.

Ira and Art gave up their checker game and came to the kitchen.

"I will work, too," said Ira. "That will do away with some of the help on Saturdays."

"I want to work," said Art.

Papa's worried face smoothed with a proud smile. "Rose, we have good boys."

Mama gathered her three boys to her. She kissed each one on the forehead.

A week later the third Gershwin restaurant was closed, and the Gershwins put all their efforts into saving the other two. From that time on, Saturdays were busy days for the two older boys. There were chairs to be dusted, tables to be set, and napkins to be folded. There was the never-ending job of washing dishes.

Ira stacked and scraped the dishes, and George washed them—dozens and dozens of them. The hot dog and bean special plate drew more customers every day.

One Saturday in February George went to work in the restaurant kitchen. He turned on the hot water in the sink, put in some soap, and spun it round and round with a dishcloth.

The gurgle of water, the clatter of china, and the rattle of silverware made a busy, steady sound, accented with strong beats from the clinking of the cash register and the clanging of the front door bell. George tapped his feet to the swinging rhythm.

"You'll break the dishes," Ira said.

"I'm dancing to the kitchen music," George replied. "I won't break anything."

Ira scraped the leavings from a plate into a big garbage container. "I'll make up words to this kitchen music." He laughed and said in a loud rag man's voice,

> "Garbage go flip, garbage go flop,
> Garbage go in a barrel of slop."

"Ira, you're good," said George. "If we ever get a piano, I'll compose music and you can make up words for it."

"That will be a day!" Ira sang again.

Suddenly George's face sobered. He remembered that every Sunday he went to see Maxie and Maxie didn't like this kind of music. Maxie's music was soft and beautiful.

When George went to see Maxie the next afternoon, the first thing Maxie said was, "You'll have to learn to read music."

"I know." George bit his lip. He couldn't learn without a piano, could he?

Maxie began to play some weird music that made George forget his discontent.

"This is a Hungarian Rhapsody by Franz Liszt," said Maxie. "It's gypsy music. Close your eyes and listen. You can see the gypsies dancing and hear the bells and cymbals."

George could see dancing gypsies through the

happy sounds of the violin. "Was Franz Liszt a gypsy?" he asked.

"No, no. He lived in a little town in Hungary and gypsies used to camp near his home. He used to listen to their music and watch them dance. The sights and sounds stayed with him all his life. You can hear them in his music."

The strains of the "Hungarian Rhapsody" were clear in George's mind. He thumped out the weird air with two fingers of his right hand. His left hand began to beat—*thump, thump.*

"No, don't put in all those extra notes," said Maxie. "You must play the music of great composers exactly as it is written."

George tried again. Again the extra notes slipped in.

Maxie became impatient. "George, you just don't have it in you to be a musician. Take my word for it. I know."

George could hardly believe his ears.

Maxie's face showed no friendliness. "You don't have it in you," he said again.

George felt weak, as if Maxie had struck him. "I guess I better go home," he said softly, and stood up. Somehow, he got outside.

The sidewalk was caked with ice. Wind from the river whipped around him, and he turned the collar of his coat up around his neck. Stinging sleet slapped against his face, but it didn't hurt as much as Maxie's words.

No Scales for George

All the neighbors in the block were gathered in front of the Gershwin apartment. All the relatives except young Aunt Kate were gathered in the Gershwin parlor. The Gershwins had bought a piano, and it was being delivered.

George was down in the street, running from one side of the wagon to the other, trying to see the piano. It was covered with several old blankets and quilts.

The piano was much too large to be carried up the winding front stairs or the narrow back stairs, so the movers were tying ropes around it. Then, by running a long rope through a pulley on the roof, they would hoist it up to the parlor window. Papa and a friend, Mr. Bloom, had removed the sashes from the window.

"What are you getting?" asked John.

George acted as if he had not heard.

"That's a piano," said Oliver. He had heard the neighbors talking.

"Are you going to take lessons, George?" John persisted. "Are you going to take lessons?"

"The piano is for Frankie," said George. This was almost true. It was for the whole family, including little Frankie.

"Hah! She's too little to take lessons," said John. "You can't fool me."

Two of the movers had gone up to the roof. Now they let down a rope with a hook on the end of it. Another mover secured the hook to the ropes around the piano. Then the men above passed the rope over the pulley and dropped the other end to the sidewalk.

"Stand back!" Uncle Harry warned the crowd.

The movers pulled on the rope and the piano tottered, then started to rise. Up, up! The piano rocked.

"Be careful! Don't let it fall!" called Mama.

"Get out of the way, children," Uncle Harry ordered, and the whole crowd moved back.

The men lifted the piano slowly. After they raised it to the window, other men reached out to pull it inside the room. George hurried up the front stairs to watch.

"Hee, hee! George is going to take piano lessons," the boys called, but George was too excited to care much about the teasing.

Upstairs the movers carefully lowered the piano to the floor. Then they moved it to a cleared space along the wall.

After the blankets and quilts had been removed, Mama inspected every inch of the shiny mahogany finish. It had not been scratched.

"Now who is going to play it?" asked Papa.

"Kate is the only one who knows how to play a piano," said Grandma.

"I wish she were here," said Grandpa. "I'd like to hear how it sounds."

"Isidore is going to take lessons," said Mama.

George twisted the piano stool to the right height. He sat down.

"Don't get the keys dirty," Mama warned.

"My hands are clean," he said, wiggling his fingers above the keyboard. Could he remember how to play?

Several years had passed since he had played with Maxie. Many things had happened in the country since then. William Howard Taft had become President. The panic had passed and the country had become prosperous. Papa and Uncle Harry had sold all their restaurants and were now in the Turkish Bath business.

George's fingers brushed against the keys. He

hadn't touched a piano recently. Should he try to play "Hungarian Rhapsody"? No, he didn't even want to play Maxie's music. He was still hurt by Maxie's remark.

He pressed several keys with the right hand. Then both hands pounded the keyboard. The strains of the chorus of "Loch Lomond" sounded joyous and lively. He played it just the way Mamie had sung it long ago. His fingers moved freely, as if knowing where to go.

It was a wonderful feeling.

"George!" Grandma was flabbergasted.

"Where did you learn to play?" Mama's black eyes were as shiny as lumps of coal.

"Was it when you were with that boy musician, that Maxie?" asked Papa.

The surprised family gathered in a circle about George. His shoulders shook with happiness. His fingers danced over the keys. He sang as he played, "Put your arms around me, honey."

Papa put his arm around Mama and stood close to George.

Outside another song was being sung.

> "George is a sissy.
> George is a big sissy."

"Bananas!" the fruit man cried.

George ran his fingers over the keyboard, fumbling for the right notes. He leaned forward and pressed hard on the loud pedal, and the piano mocked the song outside.

"He makes a parrot of that piano," said Grandpa admiringly.

"I even hear the fruit man," said Uncle Harry.

There was a loud "Phooey!" outside.

George swung around, took Frankie by the hand, and went to the wide gap in the wall. "That was Frankie playing," he called down to the boys in the street. "She's a genius."

John's eyebrows rose. "That George is a humdinger," he said, shaking his head.

"I'll have to take you to see my friend Mose Gumble down in Tin Pan Alley," said Ben Bloom.

"No, no," said Mama. "No Tin Pan Alley stuff in this house."

"George should take piano lessons," said Uncle Harry.

"Isidore must take first," said Mama.

After that Ira sat day after day at the piano counting, "One, two, three, four."

His fingers were clumsy. He had no interest whatever in music.

Every evening while Ira practiced, George squirmed and fidgeted and tapped his feet. He could hardly wait for Ira to finish. Then he sat down and played Ira's simple versions of classical music. Often he added notes and changed the rhythm and made the music come alive.

Papa smiled proudly. So did Mama, at times. At other times, however, she said, "That's all very well, George, but you haven't done your arithmetic homework yet. An accountant must know arithmetic."

"I don't want to become an accountant," George said emphatically.

After Ira had taken lessons from Aunt Katie for almost a year he rebelled. "I just don't like to play," he said one evening.

"In that case, Isidore should give it up," Papa said. "Let George take lessons."

Mama finally agreed.

Miss Green was George's first teacher. She used a special practice book to teach the keyboard and scales. She told George where to place his fingers and how to move them.

"Keep your wrists high and flat, flat enough to hold a penny," she said. She straightened George's wrists, just so, and placed a penny on each one.

"A,B,C,D," chanted George, striking the keys so hard that the pennies went flying.

"No, no. Like this," corrected Miss Green.

Lesson after lesson, Miss Green corrected George. She was in despair. "You are talented," she said, "but you must do it right."

George was in despair, too. "I want to play music, not scales," he said.

"You must learn to play scales so that you can play music," she told him.

Several months later Mama found another teacher for George. This teacher used the same method as Miss Green, and she charged the same price, fifty cents a lesson.

George fretted. "I'm getting nowhere. I wish I could take lessons from Mr. Goldfarb. He teaches music, not scales."

Mr. Goldfarb was the neighborhood musician, the leader of a Hungarian band. He had his own method of teaching piano. He did not permit his pupils to use exercise books.

"Mr. Goldfarb charges too much," said Mama.

"If I work for Papa on Saturdays, I could pay for part of the lesson," said George.

"You may have to stop taking lessons," said Mama. "You must bring up your arithmetic grades or you won't graduate from the eighth grade in June. Besides, it's more important to know arithmetic than it is to know music. What good will music do you?"

George kept quiet. Without music, the world would be drab and uninteresting, he thought. Mama didn't know how important music was to him. Still, he knew that he had to graduate from the eighth grade in June. He couldn't disappoint Mama and Papa.

Lessons and Lessons

"No more pencils, no more books,
No more teacher's saucy looks."

GEORGE SANG along with the other eighth-grade boys and girls. School was out, and everybody was happy.

June of 1912 had come and George had graduated from the eighth grade. The Gershwins were having a small party in their apartment to celebrate the occasion.

"What do you want to become after you grow up?" asked Grandpa.

Mama answered for George. "He is going to

become an accountant. He'll start in the High School of Commerce this fall."

George squirmed at the thought of studying more arithmetic. He hoped Mama would stop talking, but she continued.

"George and Isidore are going to work for Morris this summer."

At last George managed to break in. "And take music lessons from Mr. Goldfarb."

Mama shook her head. "We tried lessons, and you won't learn to play scales."

Papa said softly, "Maybe piano lessons from Mr. Goldfarb will be different."

George smiled a thank-you to Papa, then nibbled at the slice of angel food cake Mama had placed before him. He would practice hard. Someday Mama would be proud of him.

The very next day George started to take piano lessons from Mr. Goldfarb.

"No! No scales!" shouted Mr. Goldfarb. He

picked up the practice book which George had been using. "Out you go!" he shouted, and tossed the book in the corner of the room.

George's eyes bulged with astonishment.

"Now I play for you and then you play for me." Mr. Goldfarb stroked his flowing mustache, turned the piano stool with a great flourish, and sat down. His fingers, his hands, his arms seemed to be all over the keyboard at once. "Here, you try," he said when he had finished. "Remember, just like me."

George had no mustache to stroke, but he turned the stool with a flourish. His fingers, his hands, his arms moved all over the keys.

"Great!" shouted Mr. Goldfarb.

After the lesson George walked home quickly to play what he had learned. There were no scales to practice now, no finger exercises. He banged away at bits of opera music which Mr. Goldfarb had simplified and played for him.

As the summer days passed, George wasn't sure that he liked Mr. Goldfarb's way of teaching. There seemed to be something wrong. By the time he entered the High School of Commerce, he was dissatisfied with his progress.

He was unhappy in school, too, and made few friends. One of his friends, however, introduced him to Jack Miller, who played the piano in the Beethoven Symphony Orchestra. This was an amateur orchestra that gave concerts.

"You should take lessons from Charles Hambitzer," said Jack one brisk November afternoon. "I take lessons from him and he is good."

George was returning from the Public Library downtown. He had been working on a current events notebook for one of his classes.

"Hambitzer probably wouldn't bother with me," said George, "but I'd give an eye tooth to take lessons from him."

"He's a real musician," said Jack. "He can

play any instrument in the orchestra. He plays in the orchestra at the Waldorf-Astoria Hotel. He has thirty-two pupils, but he might find time to teach you. Let's go to see him."

The boys cut across Central Park. It was fun shuffling through the crunchy brown leaves that covered the hard ground.

Mr. Hambitzer's studio was on Morningside Avenue. It was a large, almost bare room. Papers littered a long table, several straight chairs, and the floor.

"Let me hear you play," Mr. Hambitzer said after Jack had told him about George's interest in music.

George rubbed his hands together. What should he play? "Alexander's Ragtime Band?" That was the most popular song in New York City at the moment. "William Tell?" He thought of the story of the Swiss patriot who had freed his people by shooting an apple from his young son's head with an arrow. He was always stirred by the rousing, fear-filled music.

He looked up at Mr. Hambitzer and said, "I shall play the 'Overture to William Tell.'"

He pounded the keys. He slapped the keys. He crossed his hands and swung his elbows, the way Mr. Goldfarb had taught him. When he finished, he swung around to see how Mr. Hambitzer liked his playing.

Mr. Hambitzer's face was pinched with deep wrinkles, but there was a bright gleam in his eyes. He said, "Let us go to the man who taught you to play like that. We'll shoot him—and without an apple on his head."

George laughed. Mr. Hambitzer laughed, too, and placed his hands on George's shoulders. "You'll make a musician. I'll teach you, and without charge."

George lowered his head so that the tears wouldn't show. At last someone believed in him.

Again George began to practice scales and finger exercises and wrist movements, but this time it was different. "I like Mr. Hambitzer so much I would play the piano with my toes if he asked me to," he told Jack.

George was studying harmony and counterpoint, too. "Counterpoint is a tricky way of weaving melodies together," he told Mama.

"You spend hours and hours at the piano," said Mama, "but how much time do you spend on your lessons for school?"

"I don't like bookkeeping and typing and shorthand," he said.

"Maybe you would if you took more interest in them," Mama said.

Mr. Hambitzer was teaching George to compose music as well as to read it. One day George said, "I want to compose popular music."

"I thought you were interested in serious music," said Mr. Hambitzer.

"Can't popular music be serious? 'Alexander's Ragtime Band' is jazz and popular, but it is serious and good music, too." The composer, Irving Berlin, was a master to George.

Mr. Hambitzer smiled. "Perhaps with more study you will change your mind about what good music is," he said.

"No, I know what I want to do. I want everyone to hear the sounds of the streets, the sounds of America as I hear them."

There was a gleam of approval in Mr. Hambitzer's eyes, but he continued to teach George classical music. He encouraged him to go to concerts to hear the best music, too. "Don't spend all your time in Tin Pan Alley," he said.

Tin Pan Alley was the block of 28th Street between Fifth and Sixth Avenues where the song publishers had their offices. It was a noisy street where the sounds of dance bands and songs blared onto the sidewalks—"like a symphony of new music—new music of a new world." George vaguely remembered that someone once had said something about music of a new world, but he couldn't remember who.

George wanted to compose music that would tell the story of here and now, just as Franz Liszt had pictured the life of the gypsies in his music. He loved the music of the old masters, but he was sure there was a place for the kind of music that was in his heart and mind.

George kept a notebook in which he pasted news clippings, programs, and advertisements about musicians and concerts. He also went to concerts whenever he could.

One Sunday he persuaded Papa to go to the Waldorf-Astoria Concert with him to hear Mr. Hambitzer play the piano. A few nights later he persuaded Mama and Papa to go to the Cooper Union to hear Maxie Rosenzweig. As he listened, George understood that Maxie had been right in his thinking. George could never be a musician like Maxie. He was a different kind of musician, but someday Maxie would go to a concert given by George Gershwin.

Later that evening he got out his scrapbook to paste in the program. As he was working, Mama came to the kitchen and placed his business methods notebook on the table.

"Look at this notebook," she said impatiently. "There is nothing in it." She turned the pages and read, "Clara Barton dies. Titanic sunk. Headlines only. Do you know anything about Clara Barton's work? Do you know what the sinking of the Titanic means? You have nothing here about our new President."

"I know who he is," George broke in. "He is Woodrow Wilson."

"George, you are fourteen years old. You must think about your future. You must think about something besides music."

George hung his head. He did not like to disappoint Mama.

"You worry too much, Rose," said Papa. He patted George on the shoulder. "Mama wants you to be a successful man. United States is the land of opportunity. We don't want you to throw away your advantages."

George was convinced that his future lay in music, but he did not say it aloud. He knew that it would only cause Mama more worry.

Disappointments

It was late at night. The Gershwin apartment was quiet except for George and Ira. Both boys were sitting up in bed, whispering.

"I know I'm disappointing Mama and Papa by not going on to Commerce School," George said.

"I'm disappointing them, too, by not finishing high school sooner," said Ira. "I won't finish until February."

"What will you do after you finish high school?" asked George.

"Mama and Papa want me to study medicine, but I don't want to become a doctor."

"What do you want to be?" asked George.

"I think I want to write," answered Ira.

"Gosh!" George sat up straight. "No wonder Mama and Papa are upset, with you becoming a writer and me a song plugger."

"Yes, they had such different plans for us," said Ira.

"They are understanding, though," George added. "They know I never could become an accountant. Papa says the only way to be successful and happy is to work at something you are interested in. I don't like accounting."

"Then you're on your way." Ira smiled proudly at George. "You're the youngest song plugger Tin Pan Alley ever had."

"I'm fifteen years old and I get fifteen dollars a week," said George.

Papa's friend, Ben Bloom, had introduced George to Mose Gumble, who worked for Remick's Publishing House. Mr. Gumble wanted to help and hired George as a song plugger.

"What does Mr. Hambitzer think about your work?" asked Ira.

"He doesn't want me to play popular music, but I'm going to keep on taking lessons from him." George stretched out and pulled a blanket over him. "I know I'm disappointing everyone and I feel ashamed, but I can't help it. I know what I want to do."

"I wish I did," said Ira.

They fell silent, and in a few minutes both boys were asleep.

At Remick's Publishing House in Tin Pan Alley there was a row of tiny rooms. A song plugger worked in each room playing the piano from morning till night. Music hall singers seeking new songs came to hear what Remick's was publishing. Dancers came to find new music. Young people and old people came, sometimes just to hear the new songs.

Everyone liked George's way of playing. He

added notes and interwove melodies. His little room soon became the most crowded of all.

George found the first few months of work much like play. He was excited when well-known people of the music world came to hear him. One morning Fred Astaire, a promising young vaudeville dancer in the city, stopped in to tap dance to George's music.

"Maybe someday I'll compose music for you to follow in dancing," said George. Mr. Astaire laughed as if such a thing could never come true, but George was serious.

One afternoon Nora Bayes, the musical comedy star, stopped. "When you grow up, I want you to be my accompanist," she said.

Once Irving Berlin dropped in and gave George a nod of approval. The nod made George feel that his fingers were filled with magic. Irving Berlin was still his idol and the master of all the composers of Tin Pan Alley.

Still another day Mike came in. "I knew sooner or later you would come to Tin Pan Alley," he said. George was happy. It was good to be with Mike again.

Early one morning George sat in his little room playing music that came to him out of his own mind. It was music like Irving Berlin's, he thought.

Suddenly the manager stopped in the doorway. "Is that our music?" he asked.

George swung around hopefully. "It's mine," he said. Maybe the manager would recommend his music for publication.

The manager frowned. "You were hired to play Remick's music, not to compose."

George's fingers dragged across the keys. He was discouraged because day after day he had to play the music of other composers. He wanted to compose music of his own, but no one seemed to like his compositions.

One day in early spring, Ira surprised George by saying, "I want you to be on a program for my club."

Ira belonged to the Finley club at the College of the City of New York. This club gave literary and musical programs for its members and guests. "Important people of the music world often come," Ira explained.

"Really?" George brightened with enthusiasm. "Maybe someone important will become interested in my music."

As George thought about the program, he decided to compose something of his own. He wouldn't try to imitate others as he had often done in the past. When the day came, he was satisfied with the music he had composed and looked proudly at the program. The last number read, "Piano Solo by George Gershwin." No name was given for the selection.

George looked out and saw Mama and Papa

and Grandma and Grandpa. He wondered what important people were there, too.

When the program started, George was nervous. He held his hands tightly together until it was time for him to play. Who would hear him? Was this his great opportunity?

When he finished playing, he rose and bowed. The applause was polite but not enthusiastic. He lingered near the door as the audience filed out. Would someone important stop to speak?

Only Papa came. "It was beautiful, George," he said.

"Thank you, Papa." George was downhearted. What was wrong with his music? Had it been too different? He would ask Mr. Hambitzer next week when he took his piano lesson.

"You are impatient, George," said Mr. Hambitzer, wiping perspiration from his forehead. "You must——" He didn't finish, but stopped talking to catch his breath.

"Don't you feel well?" asked George.

"I need rest," said Mr. Hambitzer. "I am going to stop work for a while, but I have arranged for you to take lessons from Edward Kilenyi. You may begin with him next week."

"Oh, no!" blurted George. "I want to take lessons from you."

Mr. Hambitzer patted George's shoulder fondly. "You have been my best pupil, George. You must go on, but I cannot teach you."

As George walked home that evening, he felt a strange loneliness. He realized that Mr. Hambitzer would never teach him again. Would his new teacher, Mr. Kilenyi, take the same interest in him?

Mr. Kilenyi played the violin in the orchestra at the Waldorf-Astoria Hotel. He was a master teacher of harmony.

"I want to write popular music," George told him during his first lesson.

"You mean jazz? Jazz will not live."

"Good jazz will live," said George. "I want to compose something better than the jazz of the popular songs. I want to put the sounds of America in my music."

"That's a worthy ambition, but the sounds of America are harmonious. Jazz has little harmony," said Mr. Kilenyi.

No one seemed to understand, George thought. Somehow he must make people know what he meant through his music.

As the months passed George studied harmony, theory, and music writing under Kilenyi. During the day he played the piano at work, and at night he practiced and composed. Mama grew worried because he was pale and thin.

One Sunday morning she stood beside him at the piano. "Why don't you stop studying and practicing? You are getting nowhere with your music. You could go to work for Grandpa."

"Mama, I could never do that," said George, walking wearily to his room. He opened a folder of sheet music that he had just composed. The little black dots and bars on the sheets formed a new pattern of music. He studied the pattern, hearing its sounds, its harmonies, its quick broken rhythms, in his mind.

"If a music publisher would buy just one piece of my music, perhaps Mama would feel more kindly toward my work," he thought.

Tomorrow once again, he determined, he would try to sell something.

George Felt Defeated

George was dressed in a new dark blue serge suit. He had bought the suit with his own money. He stood between Ira and Art with the rest of the family, watching and listening.

His Aunt Kate was getting married. The Gershwins, the Bruskins, the Wolpins, their friends and relatives, and the friends and relatives of the bridegroom were gathered in the beautiful ballroom of the Grand Central Hotel.

At one end of the ballroom a canopy was raised on standards. This was a symbol of home and happiness. Under the canopy the rabbi stood before the bride and groom.

Aunt Kate looked lovely in a long white lace dress. She wore a misty white veil.

The rabbi chanted a blessing, which reminded George of a song. It made him think of the music he had heard years before in the cries of the rag man and peddlers on the street. As he listened, he sensed a new melody taking shape in his mind.

The bride and groom stepped from under the canopy and walked down an aisle. Their parents and the rabbi followed them to the center of the room. Then they formed a line to receive their relatives and friends.

"Come on, George." Ira nudged him. "We have to go with the crowd."

George stepped along beside Ira, hardly knowing what he was doing. He was still listening to the new melody in his mind and wanted to do something about it.

"Shake hands with the groom, George," Papa

whispered when George passed him in the line. "Kiss Aunt Kate."

George tried to carry out Papa's directions. Later he found an opportunity to move to an empty part of the ballroom near a window, where he could think about the melody.

Tum tum de tum. George's fingers tapped out a rhythm against his serge jacket. No, this wasn't the way he wanted the melody to go.

"Morris Gershovitz!" A sing-songy voice interrupted George's thoughts. He looked up to see a man with a black beard shaking Papa's hand.

"Hello, Jake," said Papa. "I haven't seen you since Rose and I were married."

"How well I remember the day!" the man said.

Mama and Papa and Jake began to talk about the days when they were young. Their conversation interrupted George's thinking, and he found himself listening.

Mama and Papa had been born in St. Petersburg, Russia. Their families had known each other there, and Papa had always been in love with Mama, even as a boy.

When Mama was fourteen years old, Grandma and Grandpa Bruskin came to the United States to live. They settled in the lower East Side of New York, where many other Jews lived.

Back in Russia, Papa was lonely for Mama. He worked hard and saved his money to come to the United States, too. When he reached New York, he found that people had trouble pronouncing his name Gershovitz. He tried to make his name easier by shortening it to Gershvin. Later he changed it to Gershwin. George liked the name George Gershwin.

Papa found work in a shoe factory in New York. About a year later, in 1895, he and Mama were married. They celebrated their wedding in a large hall on Houston Street.

George's thoughts wandered from the story to his song. He tapped his feet. *Tum de tum de.* That didn't sound right either.

"Do you remember how surprised we were when Theodore Roosevelt walked in and congratulated us?" Papa said proudly.

"Yes, but he just came to see what was going on in the neighborhood," teased Mama. "Remember that he was on the Police Commission at that time."

"Come, you must meet my family," said Jake. "I have two beautiful daughters."

As the Gershwins turned to go with Jake, the orchestra began to play an exciting melody. *Tum de de tum.* George stopped.

"That's just the way I want my song to swing!" he said almost aloud with excitement. "Please excuse me," he said to Jake and his parents. Then he hurried across the ballroom to the platform where the orchestra was playing.

George sat on the first step near the pianist, listening intently to each note. When the music stopped, he jumped to his feet and asked the band leader, "Who composed that music?"

"Jerome Kern," said the band leader. "It's called 'You're Here and I'm Here' from the musical comedy *The Girl from Utah.*"

"Please, will you play it again?"

The leader smiled. "We'll play it again later if you wish, but here's another one by Kern, 'They Didn't Believe Me.' "

George sat down and closed his eyes. Another exciting melody mingled with the melody he was attempting to create in his mind. "Yes, that's the way I want it to go," he almost said aloud. "Just like that."

George sat on the platform until the last guests left the hall. Then the orchestra prepared to go, too.

George didn't move. The players began to

put away their instruments, but he still sat there remembering Kern's music and listening to his own melody in his mind.

Finally he looked for the members of his

family, but they had left. He hurried home, eager to try his new melody on the piano.

"You weren't very polite, leaving us the way you did tonight," said Mama.

"I asked to be excused," said George.

"Yes, but you sat listening to the music when you should have been talking with Jake's two beautiful daughters. It is high time you boys started to enjoy yourselves with young people. You aren't getting anywhere in life."

George backed away into the living room. He wasn't interested in girls. He was interested in hearing how his music would sound.

He sat at the piano. His fingers knew exactly where to go. *Tum de de tum.* He played the melody through and then replayed it, making a few changes. It was the best piece he had ever composed. Remick's would be sure to accept it.

A week later, George asked the manager of Remick's to listen to it.

"Bah, that is imitation, George!" scoffed the manager. "*Tum de de tum.* It sounds too much like Jerome Kern's music."

George went back to his little room and started to bang out the music of other composers. He felt miserable and wanted to leave. He couldn't bear to think of playing other people's music the rest of his life. Mama was right. He was getting nowhere. Maybe he should give up music.

He pushed this thought away. He would never give up music. He couldn't.

Perhaps he should try to sell his piece of music to another publisher in Tin Pan Alley. During the lunch hour, he went from one publishing house to another, but without success. Either his music sounded too much like music of other composers or it was too different. What did publishers really want?

A couple of years passed, and George continued to work at Remick's. Then suddenly he quit. Playing had become so monotonous that he couldn't stay any longer.

"And now what are you going to do?" asked Mama in a worried tone.

George was not sure. "I want to compose music for the theater—new American music," he answered. "And I will."

Mama was not satisfied with this answer. She wanted to know how George was going to earn a living without a job.

George was wondering, too. He now was seventeen years old, and could no longer expect his parents to support him. He might find work with another music publishing house, but he would have to play the same kinds of music as at Remick's. Perhaps he should try to look for work in a theater.

One afternoon he met a friend, who said, "They need a pianist at Fox's City Theater."

George walked over to Fourteenth Street and called on the manager of the theater.

"Yes, we need someone to play the piano," said the manager. He went on to explain that Fox's City Theater was a vaudeville house. The show started early in the afternoon and ran continuously until late at night. There was one pianist who played for all the vaudeville acts. Another pianist was needed to take his place during the supper hour.

"Can you start on the job this evening?" asked the manager.

"I can start right now," said George.

"Then go in and watch the show a while and get familiar with it. I'll call you when it is your turn to play," said the manager.

George took a seat in the darkened theater. A beautiful girl was singing "Shine On, Harvest Moon." George craned his neck to see the pianist at the front of the stage.

The next act was a trio of clowns who juggled balls and bats. The pianist played tricky music that seemed to be part of the act.

"I'll be able to play for these acts," thought George as he watched and waited.

After several more acts, the manager tapped him on the shoulder. George followed the manager to the foot of the stage and exchanged places with the pianist.

A violinist strolled from the wings playing the "Hungarian Rhapsody." George played the gypsy music easily. It made him feel sad, though, because it reminded him of the time when he had tried to play this same music for Maxie. He and Maxie had planned to tour the music capitals of the world.

Maxie had gone on without George and was now Max Rosen, the world-famous violinist. George had done nothing. No one knew him or liked his music. Would he ever succeed?

The next act was very different. A comedian came out on stage and started to tell a steady patter of stale jokes. Then a group of pretty girls danced around him and sang a clever little song.

George had never heard the tune before and his fingers fumbled the keys. Besides he still was thinking about Maxie.

The comedian was annoyed. He stopped and called, "Is there a piano player in the house?"

The audience laughed.

George was embarrassed. His fingers grew even stiffer and he began hitting the wrong keys. The audience thought this was part of the act and laughed louder than ever.

The comedian stopped. "Is this your act or is it mine?" he asked George angrily.

Suddenly George heard a familiar, ugly laugh behind him. "Har, har! Yeep!"

Seated in the front row of the theater was Al,

the boy who had scoffed and teased him in grade school. He had a scornful look on his face.

"Well, if it isn't old Georgie Porgie!" Al sneered at George. "So you're still trying to play the piano."

George jumped up and fled from the theater. He was hot with shame and at the same time shaking with anger. He walked around the block once, twice, three times, trying to calm himself. He could not make himself go inside to tell the manager he wouldn't come back.

He started homeward. He did not want to go home, but there was nowhere else to go. He walked on and on and on. If only Al had not seen him this particular night, things might have been all right, he thought.

When he reached home, he sat down on the bottom step of the back stairs and looked up at the stars. The sky was dark, and the stars looked big and shiny—and far away! He leaned his head against the railing and closed his eyes. He could still hear Al's scornful, sneering laugh. Perhaps he had better give up the idea of being a musician. He had failed shamefully and ridiculously.

He clenched his fists in despair. He felt defeated. He might as well give up. There seemed to be no future ahead.

Stars in the Sky

As soon as Mama and Papa had gone to work the next morning, George went to the piano. Even in his sleep, it seemed, his mind was busy composing melodies.

He fingered out a sorrowful, wailing, but fast-moving composition. He worked on it until he thought it perfect, but he could not bring himself to put it on paper and take it to a music publisher. What was the use?

This same question was George's answer to every idea that came to him now. He no longer had faith in himself. Every night for weeks he tried to shrug off this feeling of hopelessness by taking long walks. He sauntered about the neighborhoods in which he had lived, hoping to recover his old belief in himself.

Finally, one evening, he gave up. "I'll do as Mama wishes," he decided. "I'll go to work for Papa." Papa needed a young man to assort and count towels in his steam bath business.

Steam baths! George made a face just thinking of such dull work.

Mama was pleased when George told of his decision, but Papa said, "Are you sure you want to do this, George?"

"Yes," George answered.

"Then you can begin next Monday morning," said Papa, "but I want you to be happy."

Today was Wednesday. George counted the days on his fingers. Four and then——

After supper, George strolled over to Central Park. He sat on a bench to watch the pigeons. Before long the pigeons seemed to turn into towels—dozens, even hundreds of towels! George shuddered. Towels! Ugh! Bah!

When darkness came the pigeons flew to their roosting places on the roofs of the skyscrapers. George got up and went home.

George opened the kitchen door and found the apartment alive with music. He went through the kitchen and hall to the parlor. Mike sat at the piano playing "Alexander's Ragtime Band." Dobey stood behind him singing in the style of a song plugger. Papa stood beside Dobey making music with his comb.

"Hi-o, George Gershwin," called Dobey.

Bang! Mike's fists dropped to the keys. "We've come to take you out."

"Come along, Ira," said Dobey.

"Yes, go on," called Mama cheerfully. "Go with your friends and have fun."

Dobey and Mike hustled George and Ira out the front door. Everyone was excited.

"Where are you taking us?" asked George.

"We want you to play as you've never played before," said Dobey.

By this time they were walking in the direction of Tin Pan Alley.

"This is your big chance," said Mike. "We know an agent who is looking for a pianist for a new musical comedy."

Big chance! George thought of the last time he had played for an audience. The thought of Al's sneering face brought back a feeling of shame and defeat.

"Here we are," Dobey said finally.

They entered a large room lined with straight chairs. At one end of the room a stout man was playing an old upright piano.

"Harrington," Dobey called to the man, "here is George Gershwin."

The man arose and motioned for George to sit at the piano and play.

George sat down and rubbed his hands. He thought of the towels awaiting him at his father's steam bath. Ugh! He couldn't spend his whole life sorting towels. He thought of Al, and thinking of Al made him angry. He blamed Al for everything.

Still angry, he began to play. He pounded the keys. He banged them. He stamped the pedals until the piano fairly shook.

As he played, he began to feel better. "How foolish I was to let Al upset me," he thought. "I'm a young man now. This is my chance to show what I can do."

His music changed with his feelings. He added notes to the sweet melody Mr. Harrington had been playing. He made new combinations of sounds. He interwove the melody with bits of his own compositions.

He played on and on until Mr. Harrington finally boomed, "Congratulations, Gershwin. I like the way you play. If you want the job, you may have it."

George turned slowly and whispered, "Thank you, Mr. Harrington."

Mr. Harrington explained what George's job would be. "Jerome Kern and Victor Herbert have composed the music for a new musical comedy called *Miss 1917*. This comedy will be presented on Broadway when it is ready. Your job will be to help arrange the music for the singers and orchestra and to play for rehearsals. Do you think you can do that?"

George nodded and smiled.

Mr. Harrington went on. "Many important people of the theater are to be in the show—Florenz Ziegfeld, Van and Schenck, Lilyan Tashman, Lew Fields, Irene Castle, Ann Pennington, George White, Marion Davies——"

George sat taking it all in, saying nothing. His heart filled with hope.

Later that night, after Ira was sound asleep, George tiptoed into the parlor. He turned on a lamp and closed the door softly.

The music that he had composed was stacked in a large cabinet near the piano. George sat on the floor and pulled the portfolios from the shelves. There were dozens and dozens of compositions in those portfolios. He did not have to play them to know how they sounded.

There was a simple melody that sounded the way Mamie used to sing. There were songs that sounded the way Maxie used to play the violin. There was music like Mr. Goldfarb's way of playing. There was music like Mr. Hambitzer's way of playing. There were songs like Irving Berlin's songs. There were songs like Jerome Kern's songs.

"I've tried to imitate other people in my music," George thought. "Maybe that's why I have failed all the time."

He looked through the compositions again. Yes, in many of them he had imitated other people's music or way of playing, but in each one there was also something new and different.

"That something different is my very own," he told himself softly. "That is what I want to give to the world."

He placed the compositions back in their portfolios and returned the portfolios to the shelves of the cabinet. He handled the music gently. It might not be good music, but it was important to him. He had composed these songs when he was a child. They might be imitative, but imitating was a part of growing up.

Now he was a young man. From now on he would be himself—George Gershwin, composer.

He tiptoed back to his room. Before he went to bed, he raised the shade and looked out the window at the sky.

The stars were big and bright, but they did

not seem so far away tonight. They were like the stars of the stage, he thought—like Jerome Kern and Florenz Ziegfeld and Ned Wayburn and Lew Fields and Irene Castle. They shone brightly far away in the sky, but they were not beyond reach.

Would his name ever shine with the others? He had a deep feeling that it would, but he wasn't certain how or when.

Gershwin, Composer

George Gershwin had been sitting at his desk all night, working on a tricky composition. The sky was beginning to grow light when he finished. He rose, pushed the papers aside, and went to the window. Across the street he looked out on a row of apartment buildings.

Two years ago the Gershwins had moved to Amsterdam Avenue, near Central Park. This part of the city was much nicer than the parts where young Gershwin had lived before.

The new apartment included a large study. Two grand pianos stood in the center of the room. At one end of the room was a desk.

Young Gershwin had designed the desk himself to suit his own needs. It contained drawers of different sizes to fit different sizes of paper. It had a compartment for pencils.

Above the desk on the wall hung an oil painting of a man sitting in a chair. George had painted the picture himself. He had taken up painting and now greatly enjoyed it.

"I wish I had more time to paint," he thought as he studied the picture. Then he shook his head and smiled. He had so much—so much to be grateful for—and music had made it all possible. With such thoughts as these, he sank into a deep, comfortable chair, rubbed his sleepy eyes, and sat thinking.

Six years had passed since Gershwin had served as rehearsal pianist for the musical comedy *Miss 1917*. The comedy itself had not been a great success, but serving as rehearsal pianist had helped Gershwin to get a start.

The comedy had enabled him to meet many important people in the world of music. Furthermore, it had given him confidence in himself and in his kind of music.

Often Gershwin thought of all that had happened in the past six years. First, the great composer, Irving Berlin, had asked him to become a private secretary and arranger. Berlin wanted him to write down compositions and to arrange them for orchestras. All would be Berlin's own compositions.

Gershwin's first thought was to say "Yes" to this offer. He recognized Irving Berlin as one of the finest American composers and looked upon him as a hero. Then he began to wonder what would become of his own music if he went to work for Berlin. At last he decided to discuss the problem directly with Berlin.

"The job is yours if you want it, George," said Berlin. Then he added thoughtfully, "However, much as I would like to have you, I think you would be wise to turn down my offer. You aren't meant to be anybody's secretary, George. You have too much talent. You must go on with your own music."

Jerome Kern, another prominent composer, encouraged young Gershwin. He had listened to Gershwin's music with enthusiasm and had introduced him to many important people. "That young man is going places," he said.

One day Gershwin met a man named Max Dreyfus, who managed the T. B. Harms Company, the largest music publisher in the country. After talking with Gershwin and listening to his music, Dreyfus offered him a job.

"I don't want to be a song plugger," said Gershwin. "I want to be a composer."

"Exactly," said Dreyfus. "We want you to compose for us. We'll pay you a salary every week and you won't have to keep regular hours here in the office. Just write your music and let us take it and publish it."

Soon the words, "Music by George Gershwin," could be seen on many popular pieces which the company published.

About this time young Gershwin was invited to write music for several Broadway shows. He wrote a number of pieces, including a song called "Swanee." One night, Al Jolson, a famous singer, heard "Swanee" played at a party and asked permission to use it himself. Within a few months Gershwin had earned more money from this song than he had ever earned in his life.

Shortly after this Gershwin composed the music for *La, La, Lucille,* which became the most popular musical comedy of 1919. By now he was well known and was invited to compose music for other shows. Soon he was recognized as one of the country's leading composers.

One day Paul Whiteman came to see Gershwin. Whiteman's orchestra was known throughout the country for its playing of popular music.

"George," he said, "I wish you would write a serious jazz composition for me."

"The world isn't ready for such music yet," Gershwin replied. "The music critics would laugh at us if we tried."

Every time he saw Gershwin after this, Whiteman brought up the subject, but Gershwin just smiled and shook his head. Despite the reaction of critics, he had always felt that jazz told a story about the American way of life.

Now, sitting in his comfortable chair in his studio high above the city's streets, he thought about the future of music. Times had changed since he was a boy. World War I had ended and the United States was the strongest nation in the world. People were happy with victory and peace and prosperity, and there was a new excitement and freedom about everyday living.

Perhaps the country now was ready to accept a new kind of music—the music of the USA.

The door opened and Papa's head appeared. "George, look at this," he said, pointing to an announcement in a newspaper. Every day he searched for news about George.

"I saw it, too," said Mama, who followed Papa into the room.

Young Gershwin stared at the announcement. It stated that Paul Whiteman and his orchestra would give a jazz concert in Aeolian Hall, February 12,1924. Further, it stated that Gershwin would play a new composition.

Gershwin was astonished. "Whiteman never told me!" he exclaimed. "The date is only four weeks away. I can't get anything ready by then."

"Sure you can," said Papa.

"Get started now," urged Mama.

"Mama, once you didn't want me to play," said Gershwin. "Now you push me to it."

The next few weeks Gershwin rarely stepped from his studio. "I want an opening that will make everyone sit up," he thought. He rubbed his hands together and ran his fingers through his hair. He studied his old notebooks.

Gradually he worked out a composition in his mind. He tried it out on the piano and put it down on paper. In three weeks the work was finished, and he was ready to appear.

"I'll call it 'American Rhapsody,' " he said.

"No, not 'American Rhapsody,' " said Ira. "Call it 'Rhapsody in Blue.' "

" 'Rhapsody in Blue,' " repeated Gershwin. He remembered that once he had colored a horse blue and had said he could hear blue music in the streets. " 'Rhapsody in Blue,' " he said again. Then he shouted, "That's it!"

On the night of the concert, George sat on the stage of Aeolian Hall, waiting for the concert to begin. Paul Whiteman paced the stage nervously, from time to time peeking through the curtain at the audience.

"The hall is crowded," he said. "All the important music critics are here."

Gershwin sat waiting, seemingly calm.

Presently the curtain rose and the concert began. The different pieces of music sounded much the same, perhaps even dull. There was little applause, and the audience was bored. So far the concert was a failure.

Finally Gershwin's turn came. He took his place at the piano and waited for Whiteman's signal to begin playing.

At the opening wail of the clarinet, everyone sat up. The people in the audience showed a change of feeling at once. They were interested, excited. They liked the music.

At the close Gershwin rose and bowed stiffly. At first there was a hush, then a thunderous wave of applause. Whiteman was so happy that

tears streamed down his cheeks. His concert had been a huge success!

The audience was greatly pleased, but everyone wondered what the music critics would say. That would be the real test.

A number of musicians, including the members of the orchestra, gathered at the Gershwin apartment to wait for the morning papers. Paul Whiteman paced back and forth in the studio. "Waiting makes time move slowly," he said. "I can't sit calmly, like George."

Gershwin smiled. He was sitting at the piano, trying out new ideas for music.

About six o'clock in the morning Papa went out to get the papers. When he returned there was a scramble. Everyone turned to the music section and everyone talked at once.

"Deems Taylor says George shows genuine gift," cried Papa excitedly.

"Olin Downes says George has extraordinary

talent and showed himself to be an original composer," said Ira.

"Gilbert Gabriel says the beginning and the ending of the Rhapsody were stunning," someone else added.

"What do they say about the concert?" asked Gershwin. "The whole concert?"

There were few words of praise.

"It was your music that gave the concert recognition, George," said Whiteman.

"The concert was your idea," replied Gershwin. "You proved there can be jazz concerts. Serious musicians and critics accepted jazz."

"Are you going to write more concert music now?" someone asked.

"Why don't you try an opera?"

"What are you going to do next?"

"I don't know what I'm going to do," Gershwin said, "but I want to make everyone hear the sounds of America as I hear them."

That is exactly what Gershwin did in the years ahead. He used different sounds at different times in his music. He put lively sounds and sad sounds in songs and dances. He put complicated sounds with deep undertones in concert music. He told stories in sounds, American stories, in an opera.

From "Rhapsody in Blue," which was Gershwin's first big success, he went on from one success to another. Through the years, he heard his music played in New York, California, England, and even in Europe. He heard it on the stage, in the movies, and on the radio. The whole world came to know it and to love it.

Sometimes when Gershwin heard his music, he wondered whether it would live. He hoped that it would, because it represented life.

There is no question about Gershwin's music, because it is living music, heard by someone, somewhere, every minute of the day and night.

More About This Book

WHEN GEORGE GERSHWIN LIVED

1898 GEORGE GERSHWIN WAS BORN IN BROOKLYN, NEW YORK, SEPTEMBER 26.

There were forty-five states in the Union.

William McKinley was President.

The population of the country was about 73,380,000.

1898–1913 GEORGE LIVED WITH HIS PARENTS AND DEVELOPED A DEEP INTEREST IN MUSIC.

William McKinley was assassinated and Theodore Roosevelt became President, 1901.

Wilbur and Orville Wright flew the first heavier-than-air aircraft, 1903.

Pure Food and Drug Act was passed, 1906.

Robert Peary led an expedition northward and discovered the North Pole, 1909.

Irving Berlin composed "Alexander's Ragtime Band," 1911.

Juliette Low founded the Girl Scouts of America, 1912.

1913–1924 GEORGE TOOK LESSONS AND TRIED TO COMPOSE, BUT HIS MUSIC WAS NOT POPULAR.

The Panama Canal was completed and opened to world traffic, 1914.

Lee De Forest invented a process for producing sound motion pictures, 1923.

1924–1935 GERSHWIN COMPOSED *RHAPSODY IN BLUE* AND BECAME A WORLD FAMOUS COMPOSER.

The first full-length talking motion picture was made, 1927.

Stock market prices crashed and a serious business depression followed, 1929.

Amelia Earhart flew a small airplane across the Atlantic Ocean alone, 1932.

1935–1937 GERSHWIN COMPOSED THE OPERA *PORGY AND BESS* AND CONTINUED HIS MUSIC CAREER.

The Social Security Act was passed, providing retirement benefits for workers, 1935.

Gone With the Wind was published and became popular, 1936.

A huge dam was completed in the Colorado River, later called Hoover Dam, 1937.

1937 GEORGE GERSHWIN DIED IN HOLLYWOOD, CALIFORNIA, JULY 11.

There were forty-eight states in the Union.

Franklin D. Roosevelt was President.

The population of the country was about 128,820,000.

DO YOU REMEMBER?

1. What game with sticks and tin cans did the boys play on the street?
2. How did George come to have a surprise party for the family?
3. What happened after Miss Carrie refused to accept George's drawing at school?
4. Why did Al and the other boys tease Mike when Mike was returning home?
5. Why did George leave the baseball game when he heard beautiful music?
6. Why did George come to be a close friend of Maxie Rosenzweig?
7. How did George happen to find his friend Mike at Coney Island?

8. Why did Maxie conclude that George would never make a musician?
9. Why was George unhappy about having to practice scales in music?
10. How did George get an opportunity to take lessons from Mr. Charles Hambitzer?
11. Why was George unhappy much of the time he worked as a song plugger?
12. What did George do directly after he quit playing at Remick's?
13. How did George get an opportunity to arrange music for a new musical comedy?
14. How did Gershwin rise to success with music that all Americans like?

IT'S FUN TO LOOK UP THESE THINGS

1. How did the section of New York where George lived differ from most other sections?
2. Why did the children in this section play so much on the streets?
3. What is jazz music and how did it get started in this country?

4. How did Irving Berlin and Jerome Kern become famous in the world of music?
5. Who was Paul Whiteman and how did he become popular in music?
6. What important musical compositions did Gershwin write in later life?

INTERESTING THINGS YOU CAN DO

1. Find pictures of lower east side New York for an exhibit on the bulletin board.
2. Explain the meaning of *playing by ear,* which is named in the story.
3. Tell the difference between a composer of music and an arranger of music.
4. Listen to recordings of *Rhapsody in Blue, An American in Paris,* or *Porgy and Bess.*
5. Make a list of popular songs by Gershwin that you have heard on radio or television.
6. Name a few musicians who are especially popular at the present time.
7. Tell which of these musicians you like best and give reasons for your choice.

OTHER BOOKS YOU MAY ENJOY READING

Book About Music Makers, Bruno Frost. Maxton.

Great Composers, Warren S. Freeman and Ruth W. Whittaker. Abelard.

How Man Made Music, Fannie Buchanan and Charles L. Luckenbill. Follett.

Music Makers of Today, Percy M. Young. Roy.

Stephen Foster: Boy Minstrel, Helen Boyd Higgins. Trade and School Editions, Bobbs-Merrill.

Story of George Gershwin, The, David Ewen. Holt.

Young Music Makers, Ireene Wicker. Bobbs-Merrill.

INTERESTING WORDS IN THIS BOOK

accountant (ă koun′tănt) : bookkeeper, person who keeps financial records for a company

amateur (ăm′ȧ tûr′) : person who carries on an activity, such as playing baseball or music, for pleasure rather than for money

areaway (ã′rē ȧ wā′): space for walking between two tall buildings

arrange (ă rānj′) : adapt or change music so that it may be played by certain instruments

blintz (blĭnts): thin rolled pancake filled with cheese

calliope (kă lī′ō pē): musical instrument consisting of whistles played by keys

cheviot (shĕv′ĭ ŭt): heavy woolen cloth

classical (klăs′ĭ kăl): conforming to patterns accepted through the years

complicated (kŏm′plĭ kāt′ĕd): difficult to analyze or understand

counterpoint (koun′tẽr point′): practice of arranging two melodies to be played together

dais (dā′ĭs): raised platform

delicatessen (dĕl′ĭ kȧ tĕs′ĕn): small store that sells foods already prepared to eat

dither (dĭth′ẽr): state of trembling or shaking

emphatically (ĕm făt′ĭ kăl ĭ): strongly

furrier (fûr′ĭ ẽr): person who sells furs

gusto (gŭs′tō): enthusiasm, flourish

harmony (här′mō nĭ): pleasing combination of musical sounds

isinglass (ī′zĭng glăs′): thin partially transparent material used in place of glass

jamb (jăm): upright pieces forming the frame of a door or other opening

mortgage (môr′gĭj): indebtedness against a property which a person agrees to pay or else have the property taken away from him

opera (ŏp′ẽr *ȧ*): kind of play in which most or all of the parts are sung

Penny Arcade (pĕn′ĭ är kād′): room where musical machines may be played for a penny

pinochle (pē′nŭk′ ’l): kind of card games frequently played in homes

portfolio (pōrt fō′lĭ ō): case or folder for keeping loose sheets of paper

ragtime (răg′tīm′): kind of music with a strong continuous beat, usually fairly fast

rhapsody (răp′sȯ dĭ): musical composition irregular in form or pattern

serge (sẽrj): woolen cloth used for making clothing, as suits, coats, and dresses

speedometer (spēd ŏm′ė tẽr): device on dash of automobile for showing rate of speed

symphony (sĭm′fȯ nĭ): elaborate musical composition written for a full orchestra

vaudeville (vōd′vĭl): show made up of short acts by different performers

version (vûr′sh*ŭ*n): interpretation of something, as a translation from one language to another or an adaptation of one musical form to another